3RD EDITION

PE to 16

SALLY FOUNTAIN + LINDA GOODWIN

OxBox

OXFORD
UNIVERSITY PRESS

OXFORD
UNIVERSITY PRESS

Great Clarendon Street, Oxford OX2 6DP

Oxford University Press is a department of the University of Oxford.
It furthers the University's objective of excellence in research,
scholarship, and education by publishing worldwide in

Oxford   New York

Auckland Cape Town Dar es Salaam Hong Kong Karachi
Kuala Lumpur Madrid Melbourne Mexico City Nairobi
New Delhi Shanghai Taipei Toronto

With offices in
Argentina Austria Brazil Chile Czech Republic France Greece
Guatemala Hungary Italy Japan Poland Portugal Singapore
South Korea Switzerland Thailand Turkey Ukraine Vietnam

Oxford is a registered trade mark of Oxford University Press
in the UK and in certain other countries

Database right Oxford University Press (maker)

First published 1996

Second edition first published 2002

Thrid edition first published 2009

British Library Cataloguing in Publication Data

Data available

ISBN: 978 0 19 913524 0

10 9 8 7 6 5 4 3

Printed in Singapore by KHL Printing Co. Pte Ltd.

Acknowledgements
The publisher and authors would like to thank the following for their
permission to reproduce photographs and other copyright material:

6t Gabe Palmer/Ace, 6b Colorsport, 7t Neil Tingle/Action Plus, 7b Christian
Liewig/Corbis UK Ltd., 8 BBC Photograph Library, 9 Franck Fife/AFP/Getty
Images, 10t Image Bank/Getty Images, 10b Oxford University Press, 11tl
Andy Budd/Action Images, 11tr FPG International/Getty Images, 11b Richard
Francis/Action Plus, 12t Franck Fife/AFP/Getty Images, 12c Adrian Dennis/
AFP/Getty Images, 12b Cameron Spencer/Getty Images, 15t Barry Batchelor/
PA Photos, 15b Colorsport, 16 Colorsport, 17t Thomas Kienzle/AP/PA Photos,
17b David Davies/PA Photos, 18t Colorsport, 18b Oxford University Press, 19t
Richard Hamilton Smith/Corbis UK Ltd., 19b educationphotos.co.uk, 20 Oxford
University Press, 21t Oxford University Press, 21b Photodisc/Photolibrary
Group, 24t Warren Morgan/Corbis UK Ltd., 24b Oxford University Press,
25 Design Pics Inc./Alamy, 26 Gareth Boden/Oxford University Press, 27cl
Gallo Images/Oxford University Press, 27cr Ana Abejon/iStockphoto, 27t
Fancy/Veer/Corbis UK Ltd., 27b Photodisc/Oxford University Press, 28t
Peter Titmuss/Alamy, 28b John Powell Photographer/Alamy, 30t Tetra Images/
Alamy, 30b Nick Wilson/Allsport (UK) Ltd./Getty Images, 32t Chris Cheadle/
Getty Images, 32b Oxford University Press, 33 Oxford University Press, 35
iStockphoto, 36t Allsport (UK) Ltd./Getty Images, 36b Asif Hassan/AFP/Getty
Images, 37t Oxford University Press, 37b Rolf Adlercreutz/Alamy, 40 Oxford
University Press, 41t Peter Turnley/Corbis UK Ltd., 41b educationphotos.
co.uk, 42t Oxford University Press, 42b Oxford University Press, 46t Neil
Rabinowitz/Corbis UK Ltd., 46c FPG International/Getty Images, 46b Karl
Weatherly/Corbis UK Ltd., 47 Ross Land/Getty Images, 49 Laurence Griffiths/
Getty Images, 52t Oxford University Press, 52c Oxford University Press, 52b
Oxford University Press, 53 Oxford University Press, 54 Prof. P. Motta/ Dept.
of Anatomy/ University "La Sepienza", Rome/Science Photo Library, 55t Oxford
University Press, 55c Oxford University Press, 55b Oxford University Press,
56t Oxford University Press, 56b Oxford University Press, 57 Colorsport, 58
Oxford University Press, 60 Colorsport/Colorsport, 61 Science Photo Library,
62t Eye of Science/Science Photo Library, 62b Barbara Walton/Epa/Corbis UK
Ltd., 63bl Dr. P. Marazzi/Science Photo Library, 63bc Dr. P. Marazzi/Science
Photo Library, 63br Phil Schermeister/Corbis UK Ltd., 63t Dr. P. Marazzi/
Science Photo Library, 71t James Stevenson/Science Photo Library, 71c James
Stevenson/Science Photo Library, 71b James Stevenson/Science Photo Library,
73l Oxford University Press, 73r Oxford University Press, 74 Ian West/
Bubbles, 76tl Oxford University Press, 76bl Oxford University Press, 76tc
Oxford University Press, 76bc Oxford University Press, 76tr Oxford University
Press, 76br Oxford University Press, 76c Oxford University Press, 77tl Oxford
University Press, 77tc Neal Preston/Corbis UK Ltd., 77tr Oxford University
Press, 77b Clive Brunskill/Allsport (UK) Ltd./Getty Images, 80 Action Images,
81 Jane Shemilt/Science Photo Library, 83t Science Photo Library, 83b Shaun
Botterill/Allsport (UK) Ltd./Getty Images, 86t Manfred Kage/Science Photo
Library, 86b Professor P.M. Motta & E. Vizza/Science Photo Library, 89 Oxford
University Press, 91tl Ben Radford/Allsport (UK) Ltd./Getty Images, 91bl
Oxford University Press, 91bc Oxford University Press, 91tr Colorsport, 91br
Oxford University Press, 92t Liao Yujie/Xh/Xinhua Press/Corbis UK Ltd., 92b
Neil Tingle/Action Plus, 93 Mike King/Action Plus, 94t Oxford University
Press, 94 Oxford University Press, 95l Oxford University Press, 95c Oxford
University Press, 95r Oxford University Press, 96 Duomo/Corbis UK Ltd., 98
Science Photo Library, 100l Oxford University Press, 100r Oxford University
Press, 100r Oxford University Press, 104 BSIP, LBL/Science Photo Library, 105t
Dr. P. Marazzi/Science Photo Library, 105b Dr. H.C. Robinson/Science Photo
Library, 106 Jim Selby/Science Photo Library, 107 Sheila Terry/Science Photo
Library, 113 Duomo/Corbis UK Ltd., 114 Fei Maohua/Xh/Xinhua Press/Corbis
UK Ltd., 115 Colorsport, 118 TempSport/Corbis UK Ltd., 119l Torsten Silz/
AFP/Getty Images, 119c Action Images, 119r Oxford University Press, 120 Ilene
MacDonald/Alamy, 121 Shaun Botterill/Getty Images, 122 Oxford University
Press, 123 Oxford University Press, 124 Gary M Prior/Allsport (UK) Ltd./
Getty Images, 125l Jon Nicholson/McLaren/Getty Images, 125r Juan Barreto/
AFP/Getty Images, 126 Michael S. Yamashita/Corbis UK Ltd., 127t Andrew
Medichini/AP/PA Photos, 127 Hawk-Eye Innovations, 130 Streeter Lecka/Getty
Images, 131 Oxford University Press, 132 Mark Thompson/Getty Images, 133
John Gichigi/Getty Images, 136 Oxford University Press, 138t Matthew Clarke/
Action Plus, 138b Rolf Vennenbernd/DPA/PA Photos, 139 Steven Georges/
Press-Telegram/Corbis UK Ltd., 140t Bob Krist/Corbis UK Ltd., 140b Guo
Dayue/Xinhua Press/Corbis UK Ltd., 141 Mike Hewitt/Allsport (UK) Ltd./
Getty Images, 142 Photofusion Picture Library/Alamy, 143 Action Images, 145l
Oxford University Press, 145r Oxford University Press, 146 Norwich Union/
Getty Images, 147 John Walmsley/educationphotos.co.uk, 151t Allsport (UK)
Ltd./Getty Images, 151b British Olympic Association, 153 Jeff Greenberg/
Alamy, 155 Marcel Lam/Arcaid/Corbis UK Ltd., 156 Gideon Mendel/Corbis
UK Ltd., 157 Phil Walter/Getty Images, 161 Bridgeman Art Library, 162t Kirsty
Wigglesworth/AP/PA Photos, 162b Andrew Yates/AFP/Getty Images, 163 Hugo
Philpott/Epa/Corbis UK Ltd., 164 Mike Egerton/PA Photos, 165 Cate Gillon/
Getty Images, 166t Bubbles, 166b Roger Howard/Ace, 168 William West/AFP/
Getty Images, 169 Pierre-Philippe Marcou/AFP/Getty Images

Logos courtesy of organizations concerned.
Artwork p64: Mark Draisey. All other artworks: Maurizio De Angelis, IFA
Design and Steve Evans.
Front cover photograph: Alamy.

INTRODUCTION

PE continues to be one of the most interesting subjects at GCSE. It is the only subject where what you learn and do can directly influence your life and health.

In 2009 the GCSE specifications for PE were changed. This Third Edition of *PE to 16* takes account of the revised specifications and their different approach to questioning. The specifications no longer tend to isolate topics, but instead bring all the areas of the subject together. This helps you to realise how topics are related but does mean that you need to practise drawing information from many sources. As you progress through this book, your understanding will be tested increasingly and you will need to remember work from previous chapters in the applied questions. Don't worry though, these 'thinking style' questions will be introduced to you gradually, chapter by chapter.

Throughout this book, the theory behind PE is related to practical examples, to help you understand and remember it. The chapters are displayed in easy-to-use double-page spreads, which end with a small set of questions. Most of these questions can be answered from the double page. They are designed to help you become more familiar with the work you have just covered and to test your understanding. There will usually be a question that will require you to think for yourself.

The end-of-chapter questions reinforce the work that you have just completed in that chapter, and also encourage you to bring in knowledge from other chapters to reflect the new-style exam questions. You will also find that ICT extension work is included in the end-of-chapter questions.

Good luck with your GCSE and use the information to keep yourself fit and healthy for life.

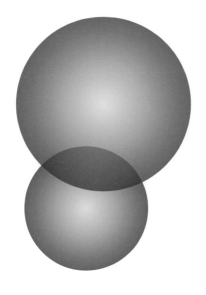

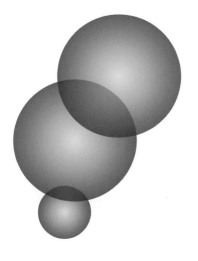

CONTENTS

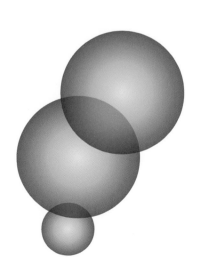

1.1   HEALTH AND FITNESS

● ● ● ● ● In this unit you will learn the difference between health and fitness.

You have no colds, flu, aches or pains, and you can run a mile in six minutes. But does that mean you are healthy and fit?

WHAT IS HEALTH?

Health does not just mean the absence of sickness.
Health is a state of complete physical, mental and social well-being, and not merely the absence of disease or infirmity.
It means you feel good all round.

Physical activity helps:
1. your physical well-being

◎ Your heart, lungs and other body systems grow strong and healthy and lack of illness contributes to your enjoyment of life.
◎ Your body shape improves – if you look good you feel good.

2. your mental well-being

◎ You learn how to cope with stress and difficult situations in sport and can then use this in real life, e.g. coping with the pressures of exams.
◎ You learn to control emotions, as in sport there is an immediate penalty for the breaking of rules. It then helps you in real life, e.g. even if you feel really angry you still do not become violent.
◎ You get the chance to feel emotions and experiences that you might not get elsewhere, e.g. success, skilfulness and the feeling of being important and worthwhile. Sport helps to give you self-esteem.

3. your social well-being

◎ Humans live in groups and we must learn social or group behaviour to fit in. Sport helps us with this by teaching us confidence, co-operation, communication and teamwork.
◎ You meet people and learn friendship and support.
◎ You get a feeling of worth, i.e. that you are of some value in society.

These kinds of well-being are all related. If you get injured in a car accident it may affect your mental well-being. It may also affect your social well-being, if you can't work and lose touch with your friends.

Having fun with your friends is part of a healthy lifestyle. But are you as fit as a top-class athlete? Do you need to be? Could you be?

WHAT IS FITNESS?

Fitness isn't just being able to do sit-ups or run fast.
Fitness is the ability to meet the demands of the environment.
Your environment is everything around you. It includes home, school, family, friends, weather, air quality, location, etc. All of them make demands on you. Meeting the demands means carrying out tasks and activities. If you can carry out these tasks and activities without getting too tired, and still have energy left over for emergencies, then you are fit.

For example:
cycling to and from school every day
concentrating on lessons all day
doing two hours of school work every evening
helping at home with cleaning and shopping
playing for a team twice a week
working in the supermarket on Saturday
going out with friends at the weekend to a party or club.

THE LINK BETWEEN HEALTH AND FITNESS

Health and fitness are closely linked. You cannot be healthy without being fit enough to meet the demands of your environment, e.g. a broken arm (poor physical health) means not being able to do your school work (i.e. not coping with the demands of your environment). However, it is possible to be fit but not healthy, e.g. you can physically manage your everyday tasks (so you are fit) but are constantly depressed about being no good at anything. Remember, health is complete physical, social and MENTAL well-being. Don't forget this when you plan your PEP (pages 44-45).

The more easily you can meet the demands on you, the less likely you are to suffer stress, or fall ill, or injure yourself. But if you are ill, you will not be able to meet those demands. You may have to stay off school, give up your Saturday job, and stay in bed for a week or two.

People's environments make different demands on them. The demands of a top sportsperson will include many hours of training a day.

QUESTIONS

1 What is health?

2 Give two ways in which sport can help your 'physical well-being'.

3 How can sport help you mentally? Give two examples.

4 Body shape can be improved for very slim people and those who are overweight. How is this possible?

5 What is meant by the word environment?

6 Why is teamwork a useful thing to learn from sport? Give an example from your non-sporting life where you need it.

7 What is fitness?

8 In terms of physical exercise, compare the environment for one week between yourself, a non-sporty adult you know and a high-level sportsperson.

Discussion work

9 'Sport is all about testing your skill within the rules.' 'If you cheat, you only cheat yourself.' 'Sport is all about winning.' What do these mean and which one do you agree with?

1.2   WHY EXERCISE?

• • • • In this unit you will learn the benefits of exercise to your physical, social and mental well-being.

There are many ways to take exercise. Walking, swimming, climbing, aerobics, rugby, golf and judo are just some of them. What can exercise do for you? Lots, as you'll see below.

PHYSICAL BENEFITS

Exercise helps you to look good and feel good.

◎ It burns up stored body fat so your shape improves and you won't be overweight. For thin people it builds muscles and gives you a nice shape.
◎ It tones up the muscles of your back and abdomen so your posture improves.
◎ It strengthens your bones.
◎ It keeps your joints flexible so you can move efficiently.
◎ It makes your heart and lungs work more efficiently, so you don't get tired so easily.
◎ It helps to prevent heart disease, high blood pressure, back pain and cancers. Swimming and walking help people with asthma.
◎ All the above give you an increased life expectancy.

This shows the number of deaths per 10 000 people per year.

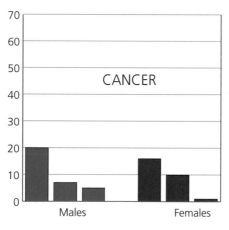

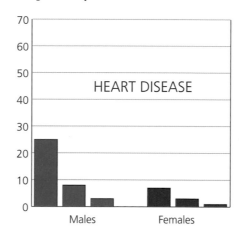

MALES   FEMALES

SOCIAL BENEFITS

Exercise increases your social well-being, and especially if it's in the form of a sport.
◎ Exercise helps to make you confident. That means you can cope better with difficult people and difficult situations.
◎ Playing sport is a way to meet people and make good friends.
◎ Sport develops teamwork and co-operation. These qualities will help you in your working life.
◎ You may find you are talented at a sport. You may be able to make a career of it or be a part-time professional.
◎ You can choose a sport that suits your personality and makes you feel fulfilled. For example, rock climbing might suit if you like to get away from it all and enjoy a challenge.

Gary Lineker is the presenter for Match of the Day. *He was also a top international footballer. An interest in sport can lead to careers in it.*

MENTAL BENEFITS

Exercise helps your mental well-being too.

◉ It is stimulating and enjoyable. It peps you up.

◉ It relieves tension and stress, which can cause high blood pressure and heart disease. A lively game or workout helps you get rid of the tensions from a difficult day.

◉ It gets rid of aggression. You can take out angry feelings on a ball or bike pedals instead of a person.

◉ It helps you forget your problems. When you think about them later, they won't seem so bad.

◉ It relieves boredom and provides a challenge.

◉ It helps you sleep better, so you feel more rested.

◉ If you look and feel better, your self-confidence increases.

◉ Success at a sport is good for your self-esteem. Success is not just about winning, it can be the satisfaction that comes with any good performance.

EXERCISE AND FITNESS

All those benefits mean that exercise helps you meet the demands of your environment more easily. In other words it makes you fitter. You can work harder, feel less tired and enjoy life more. The way to improve your fitness is through exercise.

PERFORMANCE

This is how well a task is completed. If you have a good performance, you will feel satisfied and successful. Everyone's idea of a good performance differs. For example, in the London Marathon, a person may feel that they have achieved a good performance by finishing. Some people will want to improve their time, some will want to beat rivals and some will want to win or even to break the time record.

Even watching sport can provide plenty of benefits. We learn to appreciate a good performance. If the move was creative and beautiful it is called AESTHETIC. Whole sports, gymnastics, for example, can be aesthetic.

LINKS

• For more information on things that may influence how much physical activity you do, see units 11.2, 11.3.

QUESTIONS

1 Look at the graphs on page 8. Which group of males and females is most at risk of dying?

2 Why is this so?

3 Compare the total number of deaths due to cancer and heart disease shown in these same graphs. Which disease would you say is most affected by levels of fitness? What differences can you find between data for men and for women?

4 Some people like being in groups and some people like being on their own for a while. For each type of person list three sports that they might enjoy.

5 If Sheffield Wednesday drew 0–0 with Manchester Utd they might think that a good performance. If they drew 0–0 with Astor School first XI they might not. Why?

Discussion work

6 As a sporting advisor, what advice would you give to a newly retired person with time on their hands, and why?

1.3 GENERAL OR HEALTH-RELATED FITNESS

● ● ● ● In this unit you will learn how general fitness contributes to your health.

GENERAL FITNESS

This is the ability of your body to carry out everyday activities without excessive tiredness and still have enough energy to cope with emergencies.

It is the last part of this definition that causes many people to be unfit. Imagine an adult who does little exercise. (I'm sure you know someone!) They get up, drive to work, work sitting down, drive home, do some housework and go to bed. They may cope with this with no problem for years. Suddenly their car doesn't start in the morning – they have to run to the bus stop quickly. Their heart is not used to beating quickly, their lungs hurt, their joints and muscles ache due to the exercise. In extreme cases they may even have a heart attack. These sort of people are not fit because they do not have enough energy to cope with emergencies.

There are five aspects of general fitness – use this mnemonic to help you: **S**trong **M**en **S**how **F**it **B**odies:

1 *Stamina/endurance/cardiovascular fitness.* This is the ability to exercise the entire body for long periods of time, e.g. walking to the train station, jogging, aerobics. The word cardiovascular means heart and blood vessels. You can never separate these areas as they are interdependant to get oxygen into the body, distribute it and get carbon dioxide out.

2 *Muscular endurance.* This is the ability of muscles to maintain and repeat contractions without getting tired. Many activities need both kinds of endurance. For example, stacking shelves all day long in a shop, swimming or jogging.

3 *Strength.* This is the amount of force a muscle can exert against a resistance. You need strength to lift a suitcase or push in a rugby scrum. If you have too little strength you risk injury when you lift, pull or push things.

4 *Flexibility or suppleness.* This is the range of movement at a joint. You need flexibility for tying your shoe laces, reaching up to a shelf, or playing sports. If you have poor flexibility you move stiffly and are more likely to injure your tendons and ligaments in violent movements.

5 *Body composition.* This is the percentage of body weight which is fat, muscle and bone. If we have too much fat or excess weight we put a strain upon our vital organs. It also leads to a greater chance of disease. This area will be discussed in greater detail in units 1.6 and 4.2.

General fitness includes being able to cope with emergencies.

Flexibility can be tested, in this example by how close to or past your feet you can reach. (The sit-and-reach test.)

GENERAL FITNESS AND HEALTH

General fitness is sometimes called **health-related fitness** because it helps to keep you healthy. It helps to protect you against accidents, heart disease, stress, muscle injury and other health problems. We all need a minimum level of general fitness, just to cope with everyday life. Methods of training will be discussed in a later chapter but, briefly, three lots of exercise lasting

A PE or games lesson.

Doing everyday chores with extra effort.

at least twenty minutes per week is really the minimum we need. This exercise should use as much of the body as possible and make you out of breath. It should include a stretching session before or afterwards. A good example of this type of exercise is a sport such as netball. It lasts from thirty minutes (school game) to an hour and makes you out of breath (improves stamina). You use your muscles repeatedly (muscular endurance). You jump, sprint and throw (strength). You use energy and burn up calories (helps you towards a good body composition) and you warm up and cool down (improves flexibility).

Remember you must do exercise three times a week. PE is compulsory at school so that is one occasion. Join at least one club that practises weekly, e.g. badminton. Finally, do something at the weekend. Join up with a friend to make it enjoyable. If you are going shopping, walk there quickly or get off the bus a couple of stops early. Twenty minutes FAST walking is ideal.

A club match.

For a higher level of sport you need a higher level of fitness in the areas mentioned, e.g. if you are a long-distance walker/runner you will need to work hard on your cardiovascular fitness. In most sports increased flexibility not only prevents injury but also improves performance, e.g. good flexibility around the shoulder will improve technique for javelin throwing or the butterfly swimming stroke, which will allow greater force to be transmitted. You also need specific skills or skill-related fitness which is discussed on the next page.

LINKS

For more information on initiatives providing opportunities to become involved in physical activities, see unit 11.4.

QUESTIONS

1 What area of fitness helps with our everyday life and health?

2 Give a definition of your answer to question 1.

3 What are the five aspects of general fitness?

4 Which of the following would you say need stamina: aerobics, swimming, press-ups, skiing, sit-ups? Explain each answer.

5 Why would jogging need cardiovascular fitness and muscular endurance?

6 Elderly people lose flexibility if they do not exercise. Why would this be a problem in their everyday lives?

7 We know that there is a danger in having too much fat. Do you think it could be possible to have too much muscle?

Discussion work

8 Discuss the relative importance of the five areas of health-related fitness to: gymnastics, long-distance running and hockey.

1.4 SPECIFIC OR SKILL-RELATED FITNESS

● ● ● ● In this unit you will learn the areas that make up skill-related fitness.

SPECIFIC FITNESS

This is the ability of the body to carry out set tasks effectively and efficiently. It usually requires some sort of learning and so can also be called skill-related fitness. Sports people require certain areas. They can be remembered using the alphabet: A, B, C (miss D), E, F and G.

A – **Agility**. This is the ability to change the position of the body quickly whilst keeping the whole body under control, for example dodging an opponent in ruby or netball.

B – **Balance**. See the next page for more on this.

C – **Co-ordination**. This is the ability to move two or more body parts together smoothly and accurately in response to what your senses tell you, for example when climbing you see a hold, or small ledge, and then you move a hand or foot to it. You feel if it is firm and then transfer your body weight to it.

E – **Explosive power**. This is the ability to do strength performances quickly. Power = strength × speed. For example, you need power to hit the ball hard in tennis, to throw a discus or do a karate chop.

F – (fast) **Reactions**. This is the time taken between the presentation of a stimulus and the onset of movement. A stimulus is something that causes us to act in some way. For example, a hot oven could be the stimulus that makes us move our hands quickly away from it. The noise of the starting gun is the stimulus that makes us start running in the sprints. The quicker we can move in response to the stimulus, the quicker our reactions are.

G – (good) **Timing**. This is the ability to correctly time your movement in response to what is going on around you, for example choosing to tackle when the ball is slightly away from your opponent's feet in football.

H – (high) **Speed**. This relates to the different rates at which a person is able to perform a movement or cover distance in a short period of time. This means speed is needed to move either your whole body (e.g. the run up in the long jump) or just a bit of it (e.g. upper body, shoulder and arm for a strong shot in tennis).

This needs an exceptionally good sense of balance . . .

. . . this needs explosive strength

. . . and this needs a fast reaction time.

◎ **Balance.** This is the ability to retain the centre of mass above the base of support.

The base of support is the area in touch with the ground or an object. The bigger your base of support, the more stable you are, i.e. you are better balanced.

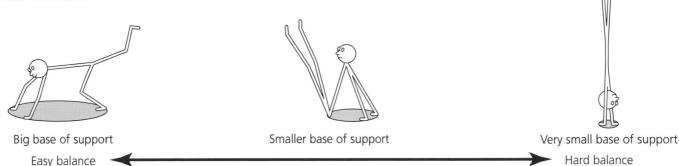

| Big base of support | Smaller base of support | Very small base of support |
| Easy balance | | Hard balance |

Your centre of mass is the part of you that is the middle of your weight. The centre of mass of a ruler:

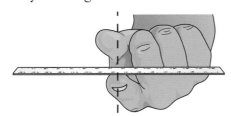

If you do this, i.e. balance a ruler on your finger, you have to find its centre of mass. Only a small amount is touching your finger (small base of support). When the centre of mass (the middle of the ruler) is directly above the base of support you get a balance. If you put the centre of mass outside/away from the base of support it falls off, i.e. overbalances.

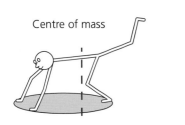

Centre of mass

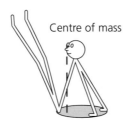

Centre of mass

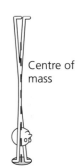

Centre of mass

In all the above diagrams the centre of mass is directly over the base of support so the gymnast can balance.

If the person doing the handstand leans too far one way, their centre of mass is no longer over the base of support and they overbalance. Remember – balance can be static (still) as the examples above or dynamic (moving), e.g. a sequence on the beam in gymnastics.

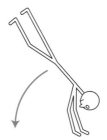

QUESTIONS

1 In the sport you are doing now, try to give a good example of when you require power, agility, co-ordination, quick reactions, speed, timing and balance.

2 In contact sports (e.g. rugby) when a player expects to be tackled they normally put their feet wide apart and lower their centre of mass. Why do you think this is?

Discussion work

3 Discuss the relative importance of the various skill-related fitness areas in helping someone become: **a** a top high jumper **b** a top rugby player.

1.5   FACTORS AFFECTING FITNESS

• • • • In this unit you will learn that many factors affect our potential fitness.

1 Age

You are usually at your fittest in your twenties. The graph below shows fitness in terms of oxygen used per kilogram of body weight. The more you use, the fitter you are (page 113).

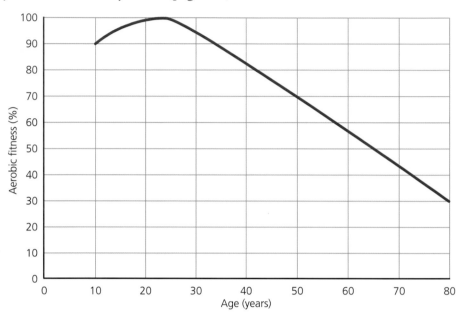

Aerobic fitness (%) vs Age (years)

From your thirties onwards, fitness falls because:

◎ muscles get weaker
◎ bones get lighter
◎ heart rate decreases
◎ joints get stiffer
◎ movements get slower
◎ body fat increases.

But exercise can slow these changes down and even reverse them.

2 Gender

Up to about age 11, males and females are equal in terms of general fitness. But things change from then on...

◎ **Strength.** Males grow about 50% stronger than females because they have more muscle. The male hormone testosterone promotes the growth of muscle and bone. It is released at puberty.

◎ **Cardiovascular endurance.** Males are better than females at transporting oxygen. They have larger hearts and lungs and more blood. Their red blood cells contain more haemoglobin, which is the oxygen carrier.

◎ **Bone structure.** Males are usually larger and heavier than females because they have bigger bones. They also have a narrower pelvis. This makes it easier to transmit power between the legs and trunk, an advantage in most sports.

◎ **Speed.** Because they have longer bones and bigger muscles, males can move faster. This means they also generate more power.

◎ **Flexibility.** Females score higher for flexibility. Females of all ages tend to be more flexible than males.

◎ **Body composition.** Females usually have more body fat than males. Fat acts as padding and keeps you warm, but it is extra weight to carry round. It puts extra strain on the heart, joints and muscles.

◎ **Menstruation** (periods). This can affect the performance for some.

◎ **Pregnancy**. Breaks from training would have to be taken during pregnancy which will result in a reverse in the level of fitness.

3 Physique

Your build and shape make you fitter for some sports than others.
A tall thin person is probably more suited to basketball than boxing. Find out more about sport and build in the next unit.

4 Diet

Your body needs certain substances for energy, growth and repair.
You get them from food. If you don't eat a healthy diet your body won't function properly.
You can find out about eating for fitness in units 4.1, 4.2 and 4.3.

5 Exercise

No matter how unfit you are, regular exercise will make you fitter.
Discover how training affects your body in unit 8.3.

6 Physical disability

A disability means part of your body does not function properly.

But exercise can keep the rest of the body very fit. Many disabled people are first-class athletes.

Many disabled people are first class athletes.

7 Illness and fatigue

When you are tired or ill you are less fit for any activity.

8 Drug-taking

Alcohol, cigarettes and many other substances lower your fitness.

See units 4.4 and 4.5 for more about drugs.

9 Stress

Exams, quarrels, overwork, money problems – all these can lead to stress. Continual stress will affect your health, causing high blood pressure and heart disease. It is also linked to cancer.
Short-term stress can affect your perfomance in sports events.
Your muscles are tense, you can't concentrate, you make mistakes.
One good way to deal with stress is to practise relaxation.

10 The environment

Fumes from traffic and factories, over long periods of time, will damage your lungs and make breathing difficult. This means your fitness suffers.
Your performance in a sports event is also affected by the environment.
For example on a hot, humid day you can overheat, which makes you weak and dizzy. And think what a windy day can do to a tennis match.
At high altitudes the air is 'thinner', so you must breathe harder to get enough oxygen. To perform well in sport at high altitudes you first need time to adapt.

In windsurfing, wind speed has a dramatic effect on performance.

QUESTIONS

1 About what age are people usually at their fittest?
2 Explain how males and females differ in terms of:
   a strength **b** oxygen transport **c** body fat
3 How might stress affect your performance in sport?

4 Explain how pollution can affect fitness.
5 Could a person be fitter at 40 than at 20? Explain.

Discussion work

6 Discuss in depth why marathon runners tend to peak in their late twenties rather than their early twenties.

1.6 SOMATOTYPING

● ● ● ● In this unit you will learn how your build can affect your performance.

Would you make a good gymnast? Or a good wrestler? Top level success in a sport depends to a large extent on your build. We inherit our body shape from our parents but we can train to get stronger bone and muscle and reduce fat.

Somatotyping is a way to describe build. It looks at how fat, how muscular and how linear you are, in that order. This shows the extreme examples:

Extreme endomorph

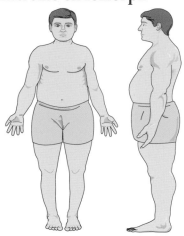

◎ wide hips and narrow shoulders (pear-shaped)
◎ a lot of fat on the body
◎ a lot of fat on the upper arms and thighs
◎ quite slim wrists and ankles

Endomorphs stay pear-shaped even when they lose weight.

Extreme mesomorph

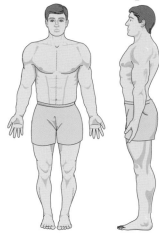

◎ broad shoulders and narrow hips (wedge-shaped)
◎ a large head
◎ a muscular body
◎ strong forearms and thighs

Mesomorphs have muscles.

Extreme ectomorph

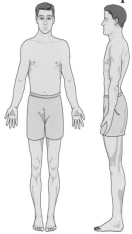

◎ very little body fat
◎ narrow shoulders and hips
◎ a thin face and high forehead
◎ a thin narrow chest and abdomen
◎ thin legs and arms
◎ very little muscle or body fat

Ectomorphs are thin and often tall.

SPORT AND SOMATOTYPES

In any sport where you have to lift your body weight (jumping) or take it over long distances, you want to be as light as possible whilst still retaining muscle strength. The ideal weight is called optimum weight. Look at the sizes of people's wrists in your group. This is an indicator of frame size. Bone and muscle are very heavy and you would waste a lot of energy carrying large ones when doing long distance running. On the other hand, if you have too little muscle you would not have the muscular endurance to run long distances. The ideal build for a long-distance runner is ectomorph with some mesomorph.

Long-distance runners need strength with no excess body weight.

People whose sports require throwing or jumping need long levers (long bones). The longer the lever the more force or power you can give to the throwing object. Think of the differences in power when hitting with a rounders bat compared to a softball bat, i.e. a short lever compared to a long one. However, you still require muscles to help you generate the explosive strength. The ideal build is mesomorph with ectomorph.

In sports requiring balance, e.g. gymnastics, it is best to have short levers because then your centre of mass stays nearer to the middle of your body and helps you balance. The ideal build is mesomorph.

Javelin throwers need long levers.

Finally, in sports where there is contact, it is better to have plenty of body weight. In just about every sport it is best if this extra weight is muscle rather than fat. Rugby players who are in the front row of the scrum tend to be very muscular, heavy and shorter than the rest of the team. This helps them to knock others over and keep well balanced themselves.

SOMATOTYPING TOP ATHLETES

This shows that at a top level optimum weight is important and it depends upon some things that are out of our control, e.g. height and bone structure. The chart below shows average ratings for top male athletes.

They are all towards the mesomorph end. That proves the importance of muscle at this level! As you'd expect, weight lifters, wrestlers and weight throwers are more endomorphic than other athletes.

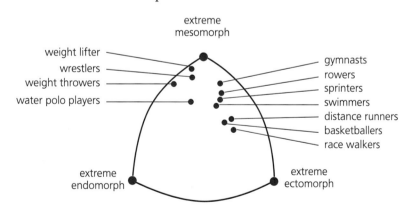

extreme mesomorph

weight lifter
wrestlers
weight throwers
water polo players

gymnasts
rowers
sprinters
swimmers
distance runners
basketballers
race walkers

extreme endomorph

extreme ectomorph

Rugby prop forwards need a low centre of mass.

QUESTIONS

1 What is **somatotyping**?

2 Which body build has: **a** most muscle? **b** most fat? **c** least muscle and fat?

3 Can you change your build completely? Explain.

4 Discuss what the ideal build would be for: **a** a hurdler? **b** a long jumper? **c** a jockey?

Discussion work

5 Discuss any other advantages an athlete could gain from having an 'ideal build'. Think about sponsorship and media attention.

1.7 GETTING STARTED - TESTING STAMINA

•••• In this unit you will learn to assess your current levels of aerobic fitness.

We now know that we need to be healthy and that to do sport we need to work on certain areas of fitness. We know our build and other factors can affect how much physical activity we do and to what level.

But how do you get started on a fitness programme? An important aspect is to know how fit you are at the moment. The rest of this unit is about how to test stamina – a combination of heart, lungs and blood vessels, i.e. your whole cardiovascular system.

TESTING AEROBIC FITNESS

(i.e. stamina or cardiovascular endurance).
The only foolproof method of doing this is in a sports lab with special equipment. The air you breathe out is collected and run through a special computer.

This measures your **maximal oxygen consumption** or VO_2 **max**. This is the maximum volume of oxygen you are able to use when exercising. The larger the value, the fitter you are.

A large person will generally use more oxygen than a small one, because he or she has larger muscles. To get around this, VO_2 max is usually expressed in litres of oxygen per kilogram of body weight.

Because the above test needs so much special equipment, other tests have been devised to do the same thing. They are not as accurate but do compare well.

Sophisticated equipment is used to measure VO_2 max in the lab. At school you can use the multistage fitness test (below) which is much simpler.

THE MULTISTAGE FITNESS TEST

Equipment
◎ A distance of 20 metres marked out on the ground with sticky tape.
◎ A tape recorder and a tape with bleeps recorded on it. (The bleeps start slow but speed up each minute. The slowest are called level 1, the fastest are level 23.)

Method
1 Run 20-metre shuttles between the lines of sticky tape. Your foot should be on or across the sticky tape each time the bleep sounds.
2 When the bleep speeds up you must speed up too.
3 Stop when you cannot keep up with the bleep. The level and the number of shuttles you did at that level are recorded.
4 Your teacher will then work out your VO_2 max from a table. The higher it is the fitter you are.

Although the multistage fitness test is good, it is a maximal test, i.e. you carry on until you cannot do any more. This is dangerous for the very unfit and also painful. The next test is sub-maximal, i.e. you stop before your maximum effort.

The multistage fitness test, or 'bleep test'.

THE COOPER TEST

Equipment

◎ A measured running track, in the gym or outside.
◎ A stop watch and whistle.

Method

1 Jog on the spot to warm up.
2 When the whistle goes, start running round the track as fast as you can. Your laps will be counted.
3 The whistle will go again when twelve minutes are up. Stop running. The further you ran in the time, the fitter you are.

THE KASCH-BOYER STEP TEST

Equipment

◎ One bench, 30cm high.
◎ A stop watch.
◎ Paper and pen to record.

Method

1 Step onto the bench one foot at a time and then step down again at a pace of one every two seconds for three minutes.
2 Five seconds after finishing take your pulse for one minute.

The lower your heart rate at the end of this the higher your level of cardiovascular endurance. The results can be compared to a rating chart.

These three tests all look at a person's stamina. The last two are good indicators of general fitness. To be able to complete them they will also need muscular endurance. There is little point in testing strength as each muscle would require a different test. If you were going to set a programme to help general fitness it would involve activities using the whole body, e.g. swimming. This means overall strength would increase anyway.

The Cooper test.

The Kasch-Boyer step test.

QUESTIONS

1 What does VO_2 max mean?
2 Name two tests of aerobic fitness, one maximal and one sub-maximal.
3 Which of the two tests would you perform on someone just returning from injury and why?
4 If your team did the 'bleep test' on a football pitch the first time and three months later repeated it but in a sports hall, the results could be said to be invalid. What do you think this means?

5 Using all your health knowledge – not just from PE but from science subjects and PSHE – discuss why three months of training could cause a person's multistage fitness test results to change from 12.3 to 13.8.

Discussion work

6 Could the results of the multistage fitness test predict whether you are a good or bad distance runner?

1.8 GETTING STARTED - TESTING FITNESS

• • • • In this unit you will learn to test specific areas of fitness.

We have now looked at testing stamina, but what if you want to improve specific areas of fitness? Your first task is to discuss with your coach which areas are important for your sport (see unit 2.1).

We now know that we need to be healthy and that to do sport we need to work on certain areas of fitness. We know our build and other factors can affect how much physical activity we do and to what level.

But how do you get started on a fitness programme? An important aspect is to know how fit you are at the moment. The rest of this unit is about how to test stamina – a combination of heart, lungs and blood vessels, i.e. your whole cardiovascular system.

A – Agility: the 5-metre shuttle

This tests your speed and agility. You need both of these for any sport where you directly outwit an opponent, e.g. invasion games, net and wall games, striking games and many water sports.

Equipment

◎   a running lane 5 metres long and 1.2 metres wide, marked out with sticky tape. It should be level and not slippery.

◎   a stop watch.

Method

1   Get ready on the start line.
2   At 'Go', sprint as hard as you can to the end line and back. Both feet must cross both lines. This is one cycle.
3   Do five cycles altogether, turning as fast as you can each time.
4   Record the total time in seconds.

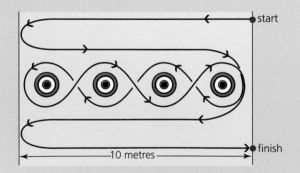

The 5-metre shuttle can be made more challenging with the help of plastic cones. Arrange the cones like this and run the route as fast as you can. A good test of agility!

B – Balance

This is a test of your balance when standing on one leg.

Equipment

◎   a gymnastics bench.   ◎   a stop watch.

Method

1   Stand on one foot on the bar – whichever foot you prefer.
2   Hold the other foot high behind your back, using the nearest hand.
3   Stand for as long as you can. The attempt ends when you touch the floor or let go of the foot you are holding.
4   Keep trying until one minute is up. Record how many attempts you made.

C – Co-ordination

Many co-ordination tests can be made up to relate to your sport. For example, for basketball you might try to bounce a ball with each hand at the same time for a set period, such as 30 seconds.

E – Explosive power: Standing broad jump

This tests your leg power. Sprint tests also involve explosive power.

Equipment

a tape measure.

Method

You may need a partner to help you with this test.
1   Stand with both feet behind a line.
2   Using your arms to help, jump forward two-footed as far as you can.
3   Measure from the line to the heel of the nearest foot.

F – (Fast) reactions: reaction time test

This is a test of your reactions to a stimulus, in this case how quickly you can detect an object is falling and catch it.

Equipment

◎ a metre ruler.

Method

1   You rest your arm on the table with your hand over the edge.
2   Your partner holds the ruler vertically so that it passes between your thumb and fingers at the 50cm mark. Do not touch the ruler.
3   Without warning your partner drops the ruler and you have to catch it.
4   Record, by looking at the mark where you caught the ruler, how far it fell before you caught it. The faster you react the less it will have fallen.

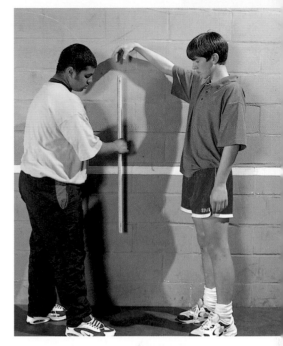

The ruler drop test to test speed of reactions. Fast reactions are needed in most sports.

G – (Good) Timing

There are no set tests for this.

Grip strength test

The strength of your grip can be measured with a dynamometer. This gives a reading on a scale.

H – (High) speed: 30-metres sprint test

Equipment

◎ a 30-metre distance marked out on a level non-slippery surface.
◎ a stop watch.

Method

1   Stand about 20 metres behind the start line.
2   At 'Go', sprint as fast as you can from there to the finish line.
3   Your partner will record your speed in seconds, from the moment you cross the start line to the finish line.

Most of these tests have results that can be compared to a table. These give a reading of whether you are above or below average. You can get tables of standard results for most of these tests. You can compare your results with the data in these tables and see whether you are above or below average. Your teacher may have tables like these for you to use.

Each sport has a set of skills that need to be practised in isolation and then with degrees of pressure. In games like golf, a range can be used allowing you to repeat certain shots with the help of a coach. In many striking activities, a bowling machine can be set up to deliver a certain ball. In aesthetic sports such as dance and gym, the use of video equipment and mirrors can help fine-tune performance.

Grip dynamometer.

QUESTIONS

1   Briefly describe tests for power, agility, reaction time and speed.
2   Once you have a result for a test, how do you know if it is good or not?

Discussion work

3   You are a coach in the sports below. Discuss what tests you would advise the following sports people to take and the usefulness of them: **a** a netball player **b** a dancer **c** a sprinter **d** a tennis player.

QUESTIONS ON CHAPTER 1

1 Say whether the statements below are true or false.
  a Gardening and cleaning are forms of exercise.
  b It is not possible for a seventy-year-old to be fit.
  c There is no connection between health and fitness.
  d Environment just means the air around you.
  e Exercise improves your fitness.
  f The fitter you are, the more demands you can meet.
  g If your normal activities make you feel worn out, that means you are unfit.

2 a What is fitness?
  b A county tennis player and an international tennis player both need to be fit. But the international player needs a higher level of fitness. Do you agree? Explain your answer.

3 The physical demands on each of the people below are different. Arrange them in order, with the least demanding first.
  • a member of the England rowing team
  • a bus conductor
  • an office worker who sits at a desk all day
  • an under-sixteen county football player
  • a seventy-year-old bedridden person
  • an Olympic triathlon champion

4 Your physical surroundings, and what you eat, affect your health and therefore your fitness. Think of one example where people's health has been affected by:
  a air pollution
  b water pollution
  c noise
  d sunshine
  e infected food

5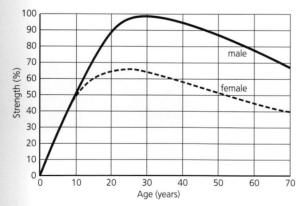

The graph above shows how strength changes with age for people who don't do much exercise.
  a From the age of 11 onwards, males become stronger than females. Why is this?
  b Around what age are both at their strongest?
  c Why do people lose strength as they get older?

d By the age of seventy, people have lost a lot of strength. Give three examples of problems this might cause in everyday life.
  e What can you do to slow down strength loss as you get older?

6 a What is body composition?
  b How do males and females differ in terms of:
    i body fat?
    ii muscle?
    iii bone?
    iv volume of blood?
    v amount of haemoglobin?

7 A comparison of world records for male and female athletes shows that:
  • in the 100m sprint, males are about 5% faster.
  • in the marathon, males are about 10% faster.
  • in the long jump, males jump nearly 16% further.
  a Why do males do better in running events than females?
  b Why is the difference bigger for the marathon than for the 100m sprint?
  c Why can male long jumpers jump further?

8 The three body types are:
  A endomorph
  B mesomorph
  C ectomorph
  Match each description below to A, B or C.
  i broad muscular shoulders and narrow hips
  ii plump and pear-shaped
  iii thin narrow chest and shoulders

9 Smoking affects your health and fitness. Below are figures from research carried out some years ago.

	Deaths from lung cancer per 100 000 people
non-smokers	7
light smokers	47
moderate smokers	86
heavy smokers	166

What can you say about the relationship between smoking and lung cancer?

10 In 1996 the UK health care system spent £1 600 million helping those with heart disease. 1% of this was spent on preventing it. Imagine you are the Minister for Health. Try to think of five things you would do to make the population of the UK more healthy.

11 In most sports, winners and losers are easily identified.
  a How are points awarded in sports like gymnastics?
  b What name is given to these creative, artistic sports?

USE OF INFORMATION TECHNOLOGY

12 Half the group should find data relating exercise to age. In pairs, or small groups, choose one of the following four areas to find data on:

i age and cardiovascular

ii age and bones

iii age and muscles (strength)

iv age and flexibility

(Typing these words into a search engine on the internet can produce a lot of resource material.)

The other half of the group should find data relating exercise to gender. In pairs, or small groups, choose one of the following four areas to find data on:

i gender and cardiovascular

ii gender and bones

iii gender and muscles (strength)

iv gender and flexibility

All groups should produce a report, one paragraph or so but no more than half a page, ready for presentation to the others. If facilities allow, then presentation through software such as Powerpoint could be used.

Other useful words for use in search engines:
Age: "old age", "growth". Gender: "male", "female", "difference". Cardiovascular: "heart", "lungs". Bones: "osteo" (bones on its own will turn up many sites to do with fossils, exclude these. Yahoo uses the "-" to exclude words so putting "-fossils" or "-prehistoric" in the search engine will get rid of these sites. Other search engines will have similar exclude facilities.)

APPLIED QUESTIONS

A13 Katherine is a good footballer.

a Give three specific areas of fitness she would want to improve during training and explain why.

b Briefly describe the tests she could use for these areas of fitness and explain their use.

c She has good all round general fitness but what two areas might she want to improve further and why?

d Katherine's build is mainly ectomorph. Can she change this to make herself more suitable for football? Explain your answer fully.

e Katherine and her friend Paul are similar in their ability in Year 7. Will this stay the same as they become adults? Give three reasons to explain your answer.

f As stated earlier, Katherine's build is mainly ectomorph. Name two other sports that this suggests she might be good at?

g Obviously your build only suggests what you might excel at. A tall mesomorph might be good at discus.

i What is there to suggest this?

ii What other areas of fitness would they also need to be good at?

h Katherine's dad, Mike, is forty years old. He does no exercise. List three changes that will be occurring in his body that will cause his fitness to drop.

i Mike's friend Pete is fifty-five years old. He is a marathon runner and much fitter than Mike. How can this be when he is fifteen years older than him?

A14 Jamie is a shy fourteen-year-old. He is slightly overweight and does not really enjoy games where he has to run long distances and get muddy and wet. He has just moved to a new area and has no real hobbies.

a Name three sports he could take up in or out of school.

b Which physical benefit would he gain the most from?

c What three mental benefits would really help him?

d What two social benefits would help him?

e If Jamie took up swimming to get fitter, how often and for how long should he do it?

f What might Jamie consider a good performance from himself?

A15 Nathan is sixteen. He has not enjoyed school and has many difficulties at home. He used to have many problems with getting into fights until he started playing rugby on a regular basis.

a Why is rugby a good sport for Nathan?

b Give two other mental benefits that will aid his well-being.

c Do you think it would be good for a rugby player to work on all-over flexibility? At what joints should rugby players have good flexibility and where do they not want it? Explain your answer.

d In the following scenario, state the area of fitness Nathan needs:

i From the kick-off Nathan sprints after the ball.

ii It unexpectedly bounces off the opposition and goes sideways. Nathan immediately responds and gets to the ball first.

iii He picks up the ball, dodges a tackle,

iv and then passes a long ball out to the wing.

2.1   PRINCIPLES OF TRAINING (1)

• • • • In the next two units you will learn the principles you will need to take into account when planning training.

You have already learned why you have to be fit and healthy. Now you need to look at what principles you must take into consideration when planning any training. All of them interrelate and none can be separated.

1 THE PRINCIPLE OF SPECIFICITY

It would be no use doing lots of weight training and ending up with a body builder's physique if you wanted to be a jockey! You must be specific. This means just working on the areas you need, i.e:

◎ Train the correct groups of muscle.
◎ Train the specific areas of fitness, e.g. stamina or co-ordination, etc.
◎ Train the correct energy system – aerobic or anaerobic (more about these on pages 28–29, but very simply aerobic sports last longer than 1½ minutes and are not maximum effort. Anaerobic sports require flat-out maximum effort for less than 1½ minutes).
◎ Start at the correct level.
◎ Work under pressure if your sport requires it.

It is important to find out how someone feels after training. Top-level sportspeople often push themselves through the pain barrier.

Pressure training

When we are under pressure and thinking of lots of things our skills break down. This also happens when our bodies are under pressure such as after a long sprint. For example, shooting a goal in netball is quite easy when there is no pressure, but it is not realistic. It would be better to practise by doing:

◎ A series of sprints, receive a pass, pivot and shoot. Repeat this ten times as quick as you can. Rest and then repeat for two more sets.

◎ You could also simulate match pressure by setting a penalty if you score below a certain number, e.g. get less than 6 out of 10 and have to do 20 sit-ups. This makes the whole practice more realistic.

Another example of pressure training could be in football where a goalkeeper has to deal with shots taken very quickly one after another from different angles. It would sharpen up their reactions, their decision making and gets the body used to doing skilful work even when it is flooded with lactic acid.

---

2 THE PRINCIPLE OF PROGRESSION

This means starting slowly and building up. Your body takes time to adapt to the increased demands on it. If you overdo exercise you could risk torn muscles and joint injuries.

You will notice the biggest changes early in your training programme. The fitter you get, the harder it is to gain further improvement. This shows you are getting close to your full potential. If you keep exercising at a constant level your fitness will stay at that level.

Both students are exercising their muscles, but the end results will be different. Heavy loads will build strength, many repetitions of light loads will improve endurance.

A good way to check if you are ready to progress and move on to harder training is to ask yourself the following set of questions:
◎ Did I manage to complete the session? For example, jog for 2 miles.
◎ Did I feel bad during the exercise?
◎ Did I feel I could actually have done more?
◎ Was I stiff or sore the next day?

If you are exercising to improve your health it should not be painful. You should feel that you have done nearly as much as possible but that the experience should not be unpleasant or it will put you off.

On the other hand, if training specific areas to become a high-level sportsperson, the phrase '*There is no gain without pain*' often proves to be true as you are pushing yourself to the maximum. Sports people are highly motivated and can push themselves through pain barriers.

When training for health reasons the emphasis is on fun and should not end up with the person being in pain.

QUESTIONS

1 Write down a list of things you would specifically train if you were: **a** a rounders player, **b** a shot putter, **c** a person wanting to be healthier.

2 If **you** were training next week (some of you will be), discuss what you should work on specifically and why.

3 What is the danger of trying to progress too quickly?

4 'There is no gain without pain.' Do you think this statement is true?

Discussion work

5 Make up and discuss some pressure training exercises to help: **a** a basketball player, **b** a badminton player, **c** a cricketer.

2.2 PRINCIPLES OF TRAINING (2)

• • • • • In this unit you will learn about the principle of overload and reversibility.

3 THE PRINCIPLE OF OVERLOAD

Fitness can only be improved by doing more than you normally do, i.e. overloading your body systems. For an unfit person any exercise could be more than normal!

Overloading is done by applying the FITT principle. We will use the February training diary of Sarah (opposite) to help us. She has realised that she needs to be healthier and had decided to improve her stamina, muscular endurance and body composition by doing gentle exercise. She has decided to try and do 20 minutes of jogging and swimming every other day.

FITT principle

F – Frequency. Sarah had intended to trained 4 times a week. If this had worked she could have overloaded her training by moving up to 5. Remember top sports people still need a rest day, but they may do 2 to 3 training sessions a day!

I – Intensity. Sarah ran 2 miles in 20 minutes and felt completely fine. After a few weeks she could run the same distance but tried to do it faster to make it harder, or more intense. Top sports people could make their circuit or training sessions more intense by having less rest between sets/repetitions.

T – Time. Instead or running the same distance faster, Sarah could run at the same pace but for 30 minutes instead of 20 minutes. She hit a problem with her swimming session on Wednesday. Sarah had set herself a goal of swimming for 20 minutes but this was too hard and she had to give up. As she wasn't used to this much swimming it hurt her and she was stiff and sore for the next two days and didn't train. This is a danger of not using progression carefully: she tried to build up too quickly. This soreness and feeling of being beaten can put some people off exercise.

Next time Sarah should still try 20 minutes but break it up into three lots of 6–7 minutes with a rest in between. When this feels good she could progress to two lots of 10 minutes and so on.

T – Type. This links well with specificity. There is little point doing long distance running if you are a shot putter. On the other hand if you can do different types of training you can prevent tedium and boredom, which can both make you miss training. The advantage is that different exercises keep you fresh and interested, but the disadvantage is that it may not be specific enough for a top performer.

Week One

SARAH'S TRAINING DIARY
Feb 17 to Feb 23
Monday   Jogged 2 miles in 20 minutes. Felt ok.
Tuesday   Rest day
Wednesday Tried to do 20 minutes swimming but
            only did 12 minutes before needing a rest!
Thursday   Rest. Felt really stiff in shoulders
Friday   Still too sore to exercise
Saturday   Jogged 7 minutes, speeded up for 7
            minutes, jogged for 7 minutes. Felt good.
Sunday   Rest

7 months later...

SARAH'S TRAINING DIARY
Sept 20 to Sept 26
Monday   30 minute run – 4 miles. Felt OK.
Tuesday   30 minute swim, felt I could do more.
Wednesday Aerobics – fun!
Thursday   20 minute fast run.
Friday   Rest.
Saturday   An hour's gentle run.
Sunday   Rest.

Sarah has gradually increased her **frequency** to 5 times a week.
Intensity has increased as she can now do a mile in 7½ minutes instead of 10.
The **time** she spends on all sessions has increased.
She has added a new **type** of training for fun – aerobics.

When Sarah feels she is becoming bored she could try cycling, or join a class, e.g. aerobics, circuit training, etc.

4 THE PRINCIPLE OF REVERSIBILITY

This means any adaptations (changes) that occur due to training will be reversed when you stop. This is why you need to train every two to three days otherwise you would lose the effects before the next session started. If you had to rest for three to four weeks due to injury or illness you will need to start training at a lower level than when you last exercised.

Overtraining?

Training makes you fitter but overtraining can make you ill. Exercise must be done in moderation or you will suffer the ill effects of soreness, joint pains, sleeping problems, loss of appetite and feelings of anxiety and tiredness. You can catch colds and flu more easily. There are signs that you should cut down on training or take a break.

All of the above improve stamina and by varying what you do you can prevent boredom.

QUESTIONS

1 List the four principles of training.

2 Paul is 18. He runs for 30 minutes four times a week to keep himself fit to play squash for a club at the weekend. Using the FITT principle, describe three ways in which Paul could overload his training.

3 Paul was ill for three weeks and did no training. When he then tried his 30-minute run he really struggled. Why?

4 If Paul became bored with running, name another activity he could do instead and describe the advantages and disadvantages of it.

Discussion work

5 Consider what training you are doing at present (hope you really are!). Discuss which area you could overload and why you chose that one.

2.3

ENERGY AND ENERGY SYSTEMS

•••• In this unit you will learn where energy comes from and how it is used to make movement.

In the last unit it was stated that you should work on the specific energy system for your sport. You will now look at this area in more detail.

When your muscles contract they require energy. Most energy is supplied by eating food which is broken down into various substances and stored around our body. This will be covered in more detail on pages 52–53, but at the moment we are most interested in carbohydrates and fats.

Main energy sources

	Foods they are found in	Converted into
Carbohydrate	Starchy foods, e.g. pasta, bread, porridge, rice, etc, and sugars, e.g. sweets, honey, cakes, etc.	Glucose – stored in muscles. Glycogen – stored in muscles and liver.
Fats	Meats, cakes, biscuits, margarine, butter, cheese, etc. Not too much of this is needed!	Fat – stored around the organs and under the skin.

The glucose, glycogen and fat provided by food can then be used to provide energy. If oxygen is used as well it is called **aerobic energy** production or aerobic respiration and if oxygen is not used it is called **anaerobic energy** production or anaerobic respiration.

A bit confusing? Read on!

HOW THE MUSCLES USE ENERGY

As soon as the muscles contract to make movement they need energy. The problem is most of that energy is stored in the liver as glycogen and elsewhere as fat. It is going to take some time to get it to the muscles and break it down so we must have something else available immediately or we couldn't move!

ENERGY SYSTEMS

Anaerobic respiration

For up to the first 1½ minutes of exercise energy is supplied without oxygen by using substances already in our muscles, mainly glucose and glycogen; it is really quick and allows really powerful movement. The bad news is that a waste product – lactic acid – is created and this makes our muscles hurt and seize up.

Glucose ➔ energy + lactic acid

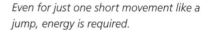

Pasta makes a great meal the night before a competition as it fills your body with energy.

Even for just one short movement like a jump, energy is required.

Advantages	Disadvantages
Can be used immediately and for very powerful contractions, for example: sprinting and jumping.	After approximately 60–90 seconds, lactic acid makes muscles tired and painful. All-out effort must cease or you will collapse. It creates an **oxygen debt**.

> **Tip**
> The aerobic system uses oxygen so it needs lots of air, therefore aerobic needs air.

In-depth knowledge

Some of you may wish to know more about this. The anaerobic system is actually two systems.

1 For the first 10 seconds of exercise energy is supplied without oxygen by breaking down a substance in our muscles called PC. No waste products are produced but it only lasts 10 seconds.

2 The lactic acid system takes over after these 10 seconds and breaks down the glucose and glycogen stored in our muscles without oxygen but unfortunately produces the lactic acid.

Neither of these systems needs oxygen to provide energy so they are both producing energy anaerobically.

Aerobic respiration

When fats and glycogen are broken down using oxygen, energy is also made. Unfortunately it takes a while to get started, but because we have so much fat in our bodies this system can be used for ages.

Glucose (or fat) + oxygen → carbon dioxide + water + energy

used for muscle contraction, providing movement

produces heat, warming the body

Advantages	Disadvantages
The body has a plentiful supply of glucose stored, so it can supply energy for long periods of time. There are no dangerous by-products. The carbon dioxide is breathed out and the water is lost through sweat, urine and breathing, i.e. perspiration, excretion and expiration.	It takes 90 seconds after starting exercise for the aerobic system to get going. This is because we need to raise the heart and breathing rates in order to get oxygen into our muscles. Activities requiring all-out effort, e.g. sprinting, mean that we cannot get enough oxygen to our muscles in time. Therefore we cannot use this system.

Effects of aerobic training	Effects of anaerobic training
• heart grows larger • blood volume increases • more capillaries grow • fat burned more readily	• heart walls grow thicker • muscles tolerate lactic acid better.

QUESTIONS

1 What main two nutrients supply energy for food?

2 What energy system requires oxygen to be present?

3 **a** What energy system would a long jumper train? **b** A 200 metre runner? **c** A marathon runner?

4 A 400-metre runner would use the anaerobic system. What are the advantages and disadvantages of this to them during a race?

Discussion work

5 A person who runs the 1 500 metres in 5 minutes wants to train for their event. Discuss what systems they should train and why.

2.4 THRESHOLDS OF TRAINING

• • • • In this unit you will learn about how to use heart rate to train specific energy systems.

In the last unit you learnt about energy systems:
Aerobic respiration – produces energy using oxygen
Anaerobic respiration – produces energy without using oxygen.

Most sports are a mixture of aerobic and anaerobic work. You may use all-out effort in a tennis volley (anaerobic work) and then slow down again (aerobic work). Every time you use anaerobic work you build up a bit of lactic acid. At some point extra oxygen will be needed to get rid of this – it is called oxygen debt.

OXYGEN DEBT

Muscles need extra oxygen to get rid of lactic acid. This extra oxygen is called the oxygen debt and **is the amount of oxygen needed to get the body back to its resting state**. Most of the lactic acid gets turned into carbon dioxide and water and a little back into glucose when enough oxygen is available.

Ways in which you create an oxygen debt:

◎ By taking part in any maximum-effort activities. As soon as the event is over, you repay the debt by breathing hard to take in extra oxygen.

◎ During long events (for example long-distance running and cycling, etc.) you create an oxygen debt at the beginning of the exercise while waiting for your heart rate and breathing to increase to get the extra oxygen to your muscles. This takes 2–3 minutes to happen. If your event is very gentle (for example a jog), you can then get enough oxygen to jog and repay the oxygen debt. If you are going faster (for example at ¾ speed), then you can only get enough oxygen for the exercise and will have to repay the debt at the end.

◎ In any sports that require a sudden burst of speed or maximum effort (for example: most team games, and long-distance running when you put in a small sprint to lose an opponent) you will use bursts of anaerobic energy. Depending on what you do between these bursts will decide on how easily your oxygen debt is repaid.

ENERGY SYSTEMS AND HEART RATE

The harder you exercise, the faster your heart beats. So heart rate shows how hard you are working and which energy system you are using.

The fastest your heart can beat is called your **maximum heart rate**. You can find it using this formula:

maximum heart rate = 220 – your age

At fifteen your maximum heart rate is 205 beats per minute (bpm). You can measure your *actual* rate by taking your pulse. If it is around 60% of the maximum (say 123 bpm) you are working aerobically. If it is around 90% (185 bpm) you are probably working anaerobically.

After a gentle run you will be tired but not in pain as you will not have built up an oxygen debt.

Repaying oxygen debt after maximum effort.

HEART RATE AND TARGET ZONES

Depending on how fit you want to be, what energy systems you want to train and how fit you are now, you need to work within a range of heart rates. This is your **target zone**.

To gain aerobic fitness:

◎ you must exercise *above* a minimum heart rate. This minimum rate depends on how fit you are. For an unfit fifteen-year-old it is about 60% of your maximum or about 123 bpm. Exercise below this will bring *no aerobic benefits*.

◎ you must also exercise below an upper limit. Once your heart rate rises above a certain point you are doing anaerobic work and lactic acid will build up and cause you pain. This point will vary depending upon your present fitness level and could be anywhere between 70–85% of your maximum. You must exercise below this point to gain aerobic benefits.

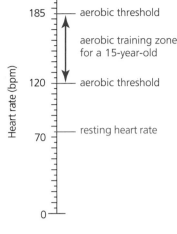

The aerobic training zone and the training thresholds. Where will the anaerobic training zone be?

This means that for aerobic training you must work within a range of heart rates. This is called your **aerobic training zone**. You reach it, and stay in it, by adjusting the intensity of your exercise. The heart rates at the limits of the zone are called the **training thresholds**. The point at which you can no longer supply enough energy aerobically is called your **aerobic threshold**, after this you move into anaerobic work.

The graph on the right shows that target zones are specific to you.

An unfit person should be working at 60–70% of their maximum heart rate, a fitter person at 65–75% and a fit person at 75–85%.

Keep this in mind when planning your personal PEP.

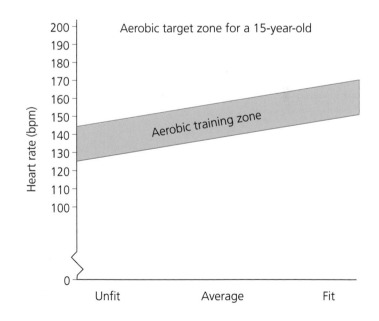

QUESTIONS

1 Write two specific examples of instances in team games where you switch from one energy system to another.

2 What would the maximum heart rate be for a 20-year-old? A 45-year-old? A 70-year-old?

3 Using target zones explain why not all of these people in question 2 would be working aerobically at 160 bpm.

Discussion work

4 A long distance runner starts off at a sprint to avoid the pack. They run fast to keep near the front with a short burst of speed to lose a couple of runners. In the final sprint their legs give out. Discuss why.

2.5 METHODS OF TRAINING (1)

• • • • In the next two units you will learn methods of training and how to overload in them.

As you know when planning training you need to take into account the principles of specificity, progression and overload. When looking at how to overload (using FITT) the type of training is important and this is the focus of the next two units.

CONTINUOUS TRAINING

Continuous training is a good way to improve your aerobic system. It is also a good way to burn body fat. You run, swim, cycle or walk for at least thirty minutes at the same pace, without rest. You can overload by increasing the weekly frequency, the intensity (by running the same distance but faster) or the time (by running at the same speed but for longer).

◎ Build up the time slowly, if you are unfit.
◎ Work in your aerobic training zone. Start at around 60% of your maximum heart rate and work up to 75%.
◎ If you are training for competitions, work up to distances that are 2–5 times the competition distance.
◎ If you have joint problems, or are elderly, swimming and cycling are better because your weight is supported.

Its advantages are that:
◎ It can be very cheap as running and walking can be done anywhere.
◎ It can be done from home and needs no transport to get somewhere.

Continuous training has some disadvantages:
◎ It includes no skill work.
◎ It can get boring.
◎ It only improves your aerobic system so if you are running to help improve your football game, for example, you will also need sprint sessions.

FARTLEK TRAINING

Fartlek training was developed in Sweden. The word means *speed play*, and the method involves many changes of speed. You can use it to improve both aerobic and anaerobic energy systems. You can adapt it for running, cycling, skiing and other activities. It involves you repeating different speeds many times. You can do it on fields using cones, or on a normal run using lamp posts or houses as your markers.

◎ Fartlek running sessions are very good for games players, since games have many changes of speed.
◎ Change the mix of fast and slow work to suit your sport and the energy system you want to work on.
◎ To overload, increase the weekly frequency, the time or speed (intensity) for each activity or choose more difficult ground. For example run uphill or through sand.

Continuous training improves your aerobic endurance – and tests your mental endurance. You need good motivation to keep going.

A typical fartlek session	
Jog for warm up	8 min
90% sprint every other lamp-post with jog recovery	8 posts
Jog recovery	5 min
Sprint acceleration 10 paces,	10 reps
Jog recovery	30 sec
3/4 pace for 30 sec	6 reps
Jog recovery	1 min
Jog to finish	10 min

Fartlek training has some disadvantages:
◎ Although the coach decides on the speed you should be working at, it is hard to tell if athletes are working as hard as they should.
◎ It needs a lot of motivation to work at maximum speed, so it is easy to drop the effort.

AEROBICS

Aerobics classes are a popular way to improve aerobic fitness. You do exercises for every part of the body. You work at a pace that keeps your heart rate in the aerobic training zone.
◎ You work in time to music, which makes it fun.
◎ Jumping and stamping can jar your bones and damage your joints. To avoid this, work on a sprung hardwood floor or soft mat. Or else choose low impact aerobics. What do you think these are?
◎ Within the class you concentrate on certain muscle groups at a time, e.g. the stomach or arms. A good instructor will work you until the muscles ache with lactic acid and then change to a whole body exercise. This will raise your heart rate and the lactic acid will get washed out of your muscles.
◎ You can overload by increasing weekly frequency. Classes are usually for a set time so it is hard to increase in this area, but early on you may have to stop an exercise because you can't keep up. Later, as you progress, you can go for longer. You can increase intensity by going to a higher level class or by using a step. Likewise if you have joint problems, are returning from injury or are elderly you could do aqua aerobics, where your body is supported by the water.

CROSS TRAINING

This is where you use other forms of exercise to help you get fitter for your sport, e.g. weight training to help rugby, or cycling to help running. It is good because it helps to prevent boredom but it may not be specific enough for top athletes.

PILATES AND YOGA

Yoga is an exercise where you use stretches to create balances by developing strength and flexibility. Pilates improves your back and abdomen core muscles by exercises and balances using your body weight as a load.

Yoga classes make exercise fun. (But isn't it always?)

QUESTIONS

1 What is continuous training? What activities could you use?
2 Name one disadvantage of continuous training.
3 What is Fartlek training?
4 Why is Fartlek training good for games players?
5 Make up a Fartlek training session for a cyclist.

Discussion work

6 Do you think **a** continuous training and **b** Fartlek training is suitable for a normal person who wants to improve their health? Why?

2.6 METHODS OF TRAINING (2)

●●●● In this unit you will learn methods of training and how to overload in them.

INTERVAL TRAINING

Interval training is where you do intervals of work followed by intervals of rest or active recovery (jogging). Note these things:

◉ You can use it for either anaerobic or aerobic work, depending on the number and length of the intervals.
◉ You can use it for other activities such as cycling and swimming.
◉ It does cause pain so you need high motivation to keep going.
◉ Since there is a set pattern it is easy to tell if someone is giving up.

It can be used by all sorts of sports people and beginners because your aerobic system improves quicker the nearer you work to your aerobic threshold. All the examples below should start with a warm-up and end with a cool down.

An interval session for a beginner wanting to improve their health:
A 20 minute jog consisting of 3 minutes at a comfortable pace, followed by 1 minute where they feel slightly breathless, above their comfort zone but still able to talk. This should be followed by a recovery interval of 3 minutes jogging. This harder work interval should be done twice more with a normal jog at the end.

An interval session for a netball player:
This is designed to improve netball specific fitness and improves power, the anaerobic system and footwork around court. Have a 30-second rest interval between the following exercises.
1 Sprint to circle edge and touch it with your hand, sprint back, jump and touch the net. Repeat 6 times in different directions.
2 Sprint a third, side-step across the court, run cross-overs to the back line and ¾ pace to the start. Repeat twice.
3 Sprint forward 5 metres and jump to catch an imaginary ball, land in the same spot you took off from. Repeat 10 times.
4 From the back line sprint to the 1st third line and back, then to the 2nd third line and then to the end of the court and back.
5 Starting at a centre third line, sprint out level with the centre circle, side-step back half way into the end third and then sprint into the circle and jump to touch the net. Repeat 5 times.

This is one set, repeat 3–5 times.

CIRCUIT TRAINING

This is a good way to organise your muscle or skill training. A circuit usually has 8 to 15 **stations**. You do a different exercise at each station, e.g. 1: step-ups, 2: sit-ups, 3: press-ups, 4: squats, 5: pull-ups, 6: ski-jumps, 7: dorsal raises, 8: short sprints.

Perceived rate of exertion (Borg scale)
A good way for a beginner to start is to use the scale below. During recovery they should be at level 11 and during hard work at level 12.
Level 6 – no exertion at all
Level 7 – extremely light
Level 9 – easy walking at a comfortable pace
Level 11 – light work
Level 13 – somewhat hard (you feel tired but can continue)
Level 15 – hard (heavy)
Level 17 – very hard and you are very tired
Level 19 – extremely hard (you can not continue long at this pace)
Level 20 – maximal effort

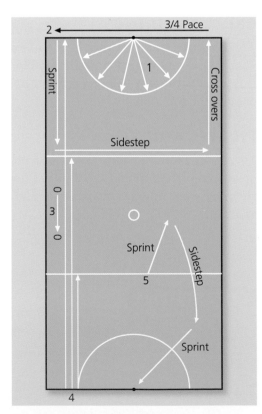

Interval session for a netball player.

You normally spend a set amount of time on each activity (from 20 to 30 seconds). You can overload by increasing the time spent on each exercise, trying to do more repetitions in the time limit or by doing the circuit more times.

When designing a circuit make sure that you change muscle groups between each activity to delay fatigue.

Advantages:
◎ Can be adapted to use free weights or body weight.
◎ Can be adapted to shorter or longer bursts of work (aerobic or anaerobic).
◎ Can be adapted to concentrate on certain muscle groups.
◎ Can be adapted to work on skills.

So what method of training should I choose?
Remember it must be specific to you, your sport, your energy system and the correct group of muscles.

AEROBIC TRAINING

◎ Choose an activity which involves the large muscles of the body and where you can work rhythmically for a long time. For example: walking, swimming, jogging, cycling or skipping.
◎ Work for *at least* 15 to 20 minutes a session.
◎ Your heart rate should be within your aerobic training zone. This means it should be *at least* 60% of your maximum heart rate. As you get fitter you can move up to 75% or so.
◎ Train *at least* three times a week otherwise it will not be effective.

ANAEROBIC TRAINING

Anaerobic exercise puts a lot of stress on your heart and circulatory system. This means it can be dangerous. If you are unfit, do several weeks of aerobic training *before* you start on anaerobic training.

For anaerobic training:
◎ Use all-out effort for any of the above activities (running, swimming, cycling and so on).
◎ Alternate using all-out effort and lighter effort or rest, so that your body has time to pay off the oxygen debt and remove lactic acid.

SPINNING

This is an exercise class where you sit on a special bike in a gym with an instructor. You cycle between 30–60 minutes and on command you change gears to make it easier or harder. It improves aerobic fitness, muscular endurance and power depending upon how your intervals are arranged.

QUESTIONS

1 Define interval training.
2 Briefly describe circuit training.
3 List five exercises you could put in a circuit of your choice.

Discussion work

4 Discuss how you would design a circuit session for a cricketer or rounders player. Design it and be prepared to justify your choices.

2.7 METHODS OF MUSCLE TRAINING

• • • • In this unit you will learn how to specifically train muscles.

It has already been made clear that training should concentrate upon specific muscles and the specific energy system for your sport. The type of training will determine whether your muscles develop more strength, more power or more endurance.

STRENGTH

This is the force you exert against a resistance. Here total strength or force is the all-important factor, e.g. weightlifting. It does not matter how quickly or slowly you lift it as it is only done once. Despite being very strong, you may not necessarily be able to throw something a long way because speed of muscle contraction becomes more important in throwing.

When training in this area you do few reps of near maximum with 3 to 5 sets (for example, 3 reps, 3 sets). Once you progress and can lift for 5 reps, increase the load or weight until once again you can only lift it 3 times.

Strength training makes your muscles thicker. You can work on static strength or dynamic strength (see photos on the right). Static strength is where your muscles do not change length. Dynamic strength is where they do change length.

POWER

This is the ability to do strength performances quickly. This explosive strength is important in nearly every sport – racket sports to give momentum to the ball, running and jumping actions for speed and height; gymnastics for height, lift and spring, etc.

Because power is 'strength **x** speed' you must also be strong. Sports people often work on strength training in their off-season and then convert it to power as their season approaches. For example, a footballer in May/June will do strength training. In July/August they will do 3–5 sets of up to 10 reps of a medium weight but each one lifted explosively and then safely back down. Again, once they can lift the weight more times – up to 13 – it is time to overload and increase the weight.

Power work also makes your muscles bigger due to the fibres becoming thicker.

MUSCULAR ENDURANCE

This is the ability to repeat and maintain contractions without getting tired. We use it in sports where you repeat the same movement, e.g. running, cycling, swimming, mountain walking, canoeing, etc.

Endurance training does not make the muscles thicker. It does make them better at using oxygen and burning fat for energy. It makes more capillaries grow around the muscles so that more oxygen reaches the muscles and they can work for longer. When training in this area you use light weights with many reps; e.g. 3 to 5 sets of 20 reps.

Static strength is where your muscles do not change in length, e.g. pushing in a rugby scrum or holding a weight as above.

Dynamic strength is where your muscles change length, e.g. running. The cricketer above is using power.

STRENGTH   POWER   ENDURANCE

Heavy weight.
Few reps.

Medium weight.
Medium reps.
Done quickly.

Low weight.
Many reps.

WEIGHT TRAINING

Weight training is a popular way to exercise muscles.

◎ It is easy to tell what load you are using, since weights are clearly marked.
◎ It is easy to increase the load by the right amount.
◎ It is easy to work on different muscles to suit your sport.
◎ But weight training is not suitable for people under sixteen. Your frame is still immature and you can get injured easily.

WHERE TO FIND THE LOAD

◎ You can use free weights such as dumb-bells, or weight training machines. This is usually called weight training.
◎ You can use your own body weight. For example in press-ups, sit-ups, dips and chins.
◎ For muscle training to have an effect, you need at least three sessions a week.

Training muscles with body weight as the load.

Body pump – weights with aerobic exercises.

BODY PUMP

This is a combination of aerobic exercise and weights. Classes are performed to music using free weights. Choice of the correct weight specific to you is important. The focus is muscular endurance. A new routine is released every three months to maintain interest.

QUESTIONS

1 There are three different kinds of strength. What are they?
2 Give two advantages of weight training.
3 Think of two advantages of using your body weight as the load.
4 What is: **a** strength? **b** endurance? **c** power?
5 How do each of the above change your muscles?

Discussion work

6 You are a top-level gymnast. To improve your floor work you want to improve the height that you can jump. Discuss what muscles you would train and how, in both non-competitive time and then leading up to your events.

QUESTIONS ON CHAPTER 2

1 SPOR – This word should help you remember the four principles of training. What are they?

2 For the following sports suggest:
   a Specific muscle groups to train.
   b Specific areas of fitness.
   c Energy system or systems.
   d Whether pressure training is needed.

   A Badminton
   B Rounders
   C High jumping
   D Gymnastics
   E Marathon running.

3 A thirty-year-old hockey player decided to take up training. She was quite active and fit so she ran a couple of times the first week and then every day for 3 miles the second week. She then started getting pains in her Achilles tendon. Using the principles of training to help you, give reasons why she may have got this injury.

4 The following questions refer to the people below:
   A Sarah – a 15-year-old girl who is unfit but wants to be fitter. She enjoys most indoor sports.
   B Chloe – a 16-year-old girl who has just started ladies rugby. She plays other sports but really wants to excel in rugby. She plays as a forward.
   C Omar – an 18-year-old county basketball player preparing for county trials.

   a Look at the schedule below. It is what Chloe does at present. In what three different ways could you overload her training schedule?

Monday –	25 minute gentle run
Tuesday –	Club training involving sprints, muscle work and skills.
Wednesday –	Rest
Thursday –	Netball match
Friday –	Weight training
Saturday –	Rugby match
Sunday –	Rest

   b Why would you not increase her schedule by all three ways in one go? (Refer to a principle of training.)
   c What specific areas of fitness would Omar want to train in?
   d What energy system would he use the most and want to improve?
   e Omar can reach level 14 in the multistage fitness test. Unfortunately he twists an ankle in a match and spends four weeks out of full training. When tested again he only reaches 12.5. Why could this be?

   f What types of training would you recommend to Sarah and why?
   g After two weeks Sarah feels really good and goes for a run. Her heart rate goes up to 185 bpm after ten minutes and she has to stop because her muscles hurt so much. What has happened?
   h Omar needs anaerobic training and needs to be in his anaerobic threshold whilst doing interval training. What does this mean?
   i Omar weight trains three times a week.
      a What kind of strength do you think he needs?
      b Which of the following do you think is his schedule and why?
         i Heavy weights, few repetitions
         ii Light weights, many repetitions
         iii Medium weight, medium repetitions, fast.

5 If you could not get to a weight-training gym could you still do weight training? How?

6 Why should you not do weight training below the age of sixteen?

7 Devise an eight-station skill circuit that you could give either
   a a netball team
   b a basketball team
   c a rounders team
   d a cricket team.

8 A footballer has been out of training for a month with an ankle injury. She wants to improve her stamina but cannot put her full weight on her ankle. What methods of training would you recommend and why?

9 What energy system would you train the most if you were:
   a a 100m runner
   b an 800m runner (2 minutes 10 seconds)
   c a tennis player, specialising in serve and volley
   d a football midfielder
   e a netball or football goalkeeper.

10 For the above examples would you target strength, power or muscular endurance?

11 a Write down an equation for aerobic respiration in your muscles using glucose.
   b Explain what happens to each substance that is produced.

12 a Write down a sentence equation for anaerobic respiration in your muscles using glucose.
   b Explain what happens to each substance produced.

13 Explain how you could overload if your main exercise activity was aerobics.

APPLIED QUESTIONS

Here is a bit more information about Chloe (question 4). Chloe is a rugby prop, she has to hold up the scrum and push against other players. She will be on the ground a lot, getting up and using short bursts of speed to carry the ball into other players, push them off it or tackle. She also has to run around the whole pitch for 80 minutes. At present she plays many sports and is just above average fitness but has only just started to train specifically for rugby.

A1 What specific groups of muscles should Chloe work on?

A2 What specific areas of fitness should Chloe work on?

A3 What specific energy systems should Chloe work on?

A4 Would Chloe need pressure training and why?

A5 In question 4, Chloe is looking to overload her present schedule. How might she know she is ready to progress?

A6 On Mondays Chloe does continuous training. How is this useful to her and what are the advantages and disadvantages of it for her specifically?

A7 Chloe has a heart rate monitor and in the manual it says you can use this technology to beep if your heart rate goes too high or too low. For continuous training explain the settings Chloe should put it on and why. (Remember her age, maximum heart rate and thresholds.)

A8 Chloe could use two other types of running training that may be more useful. One is interval training, what is the other?

A9 What would be the advantages of disadvantages of this type of training for Chloe?

A10 You are going to design an interval session for Chloe to help her improve her acceleration.

  a Why is acceleration probably more important than flat-out speed for Chloe?

  b Consider the distance Chloe needs to run.

  c Think how much time she may get to rest in between each sprint in a game. Do you need her to practise sprinting with lactic acid in her leg muscles?

  d When considering the number of sets and reps, remember that Chloe is a newcomer to this type of training so don't over do it, or she will risk getting an injury.

  e Now design Chloe her own specific interval session.

A11 What would you have done differently if you were devising an interval session to improve the acceleration of a 100-metre sprinter? Think how many times they run their race.

A12 Chloe obviously need strength. Why, in her position, does she need both static and dynamic strength?

A13 When her rugby season is over, Chloe needs to improve her overall strength during May/June/July and then start to convert it to power over August. Why?

A14 Devise a strength weight training programme, with your recommendations as to when she can progress, for Chloe during the summer.

A15 Devise a power weight training programme, with your recommendations as to when she can progress, for Chloe directly before the playing season.

A16 If Chloe started to get bored with weight training what other method of training could add some variety but still use weights?

A17 Chloe could not get to the weights gym for three weeks due to transport problems. Devise a short weights session that Chloe could do at home using her body weight and ordinary household objects as the load.

A18 Chloe's schedule (from question 4) could do with adding at least one more weights session and a run. Where would you add them and why? (Remember that more than one session can be added a day but try to avoid two hard sessions following each other.)

3.1 A TRAINING PROGRAMME

In this unit you will learn what information you need before planning a training schedule.

We have now looked at why we should exercise, what principles to take into account when planning a programme of exercise and the types of training methods available. You have attempted to plan specific types of training, but now, using this chapter you should be able to plan your own schedule – or (potentially) anyone's schedule.

1 FIND OUT ABOUT THE PERSON IT IS FOR

Suppose it's for a female called Jane. It will work well only if it suits her needs. So find out these things about her:

◎ **Her age.** A programme that suits a person of twenty could harm a person of fourteen.
◎ **Her current level of health.** If she has just recovered from a long illness, for example, you need to take that into account.
◎ **Her current level of fitness.** Does she exercise already? Is she generally fit? Is she overweight or overfat? Tests could help here.
◎ **Why she wants to get fitter.** Does she just want to feel healthier? Or to improve her skills in a sport?
◎ **What kind of exercise she enjoys.** If she likes your programme she is more likely to stick with it.

Use the information opposite to analyse Jane's needs.

2 ANALYSE THE PERSON'S NEEDS

An aerobic fitness programme is the best start for Jane, because:
◎ it will make her healthier as well as fitter.
◎ it will help her slim since aerobic exercise burns up body fat.
◎ it will help her when she takes up tennis. Aerobic fitness is a good basis for all sports.
◎ it will use all muscle groups.

3 PLAN THE PROGRAMME

(Remember the word FITT.)

Frequency. This is how often Jane should train. Training should be at least three times a week to take effect. Jane feels that's enough for her.

Intensity. It is important to start at the right intensity.
◎ If a programme is too demanding, muscles get sore and strained. This puts the person off. It is better to start too low than too high.
◎ Jane should start at around 60% of her maximum heart rate. Why?
◎ How Jane feels is also a good guide. If she feels it is easy, raise the intensity until she finds it difficult but still manageable.

Time. For training to take effect, a person needs to spend:
◎ at least twenty minutes for an aerobic training session.
◎ at least fifteen minutes for a muscle training session.
◎ at least four to six weeks to see real benefit.
(These times do not include the warm-up and cool-down. See page 42.)

Hi, I'm Jane.

Jane – 16 years old.
No exercise for months.
Overfat. Wants to lose weight.
Has already started to eat less.
Likes swimming. Lives near a pool.
Hates jogging.
Later this year she would like to take up tennis.

LINKS
For more information on setting yourself:
a goals: see page 130.
b a SMART plan: see page 131.

Training activity or type of exercise. This is what you will ask Jane to do. It should be something:
◎ that will improve her aerobic fitness.
◎ that will be safe and convenient for her, and that she will enjoy.

Swimming and cycling are good choices. They are safe for unfit and overweight people because the water or the bike supports the body and your bones do not jar.

OTHER THINGS TO REMEMBER
◎ Have an easy day after a hard one, e.g. gentle running after sprint work.
◎ Everyone needs a minimum of one rest day a week.
◎ A programme will need to run for several weeks before you make many changes due to the body taking time to adapt.

Let us look now at a programme for someone who is more active: a 17-year-old male called Dale: fairly fit, normal weight, likes all sports. He plays football twice a week for a club and once for school. He wants to be fitter so his football improves. He would like to be more skilful in the game.

Analysis of needs
◎ Requires aerobic and anaerobic training.
◎ Needs to concentrate on leg and bottom muscles.
◎ Needs to work upon agility, co-ordination, power, speed, reactions and timing.
◎ Needs to include pressure training.

Plan the programme
Frequency – He already does three times a week, but it is all football games. Dale could add running, circuits, fartlek or interval training up to an overall total of 5 times a week and then progress to 6 times.

Intensity – This person could cope with hard work. He needs aerobic and anaerobic work so bouts of maximum effort are needed.

Time – Thirty minutes for aerobic work. For circuit and interval work he will gradually add more repetitions or sets which will extend the time.

Type – During the football season he will need to maintain stamina (continuous work) but extend anaerobic fitness – interval, circuit or fartlek training. He could also weight train. Variety is important to prevent boredom. He would need to find a club that does skill training too.

Swimming does not jar the bones and is excellent for the unfit and elderly.

Dale already plays a lot of football. To improve his fitness he must use the principle of SPECIFICITY.

QUESTIONS

1 Why is aerobic exercise a good start for an unfit person? Think of as many reasons as you can.

2 What do the letters FITT stand for?

3 It helps if the person enjoys the training programme. Think of three reasons why.

4 Suppose a 15-year-old wants to improve his basketball skills. Would you give him Jane's programme? Explain why.

Discussion work

5 More females drop out of sport than males when they leave school. Discuss why you think this is.

3.2 THE TRAINING SESSION

●●●● In this unit you will learn the three parts of a training session.

Having now decided on a programme of training, your actual training session should have three parts: the warm-up, the activity and the cool-down.

1 THE WARM-UP

The **warm-up** is light exercise to get you ready for the main activity. In cold weather wear a track suit and plenty of layers.

◎ Start with light jogging for 5 minutes or so. This warms your muscles. It makes them more flexible and lowers the risk of injury. It increases your heart rate and blood flow. It warms the synovial fluid and makes your joints more mobile.

◎ Next do some stretching. Work all the main joints. Stretching increases the range of movement at the joints. It helps to stop muscles, tendons and ligaments getting strained. Hold each stretch for at least 10–30 seconds, with no bouncing.

◎ Now do a specific warm-up for the activity. For example, a few tennis serves or some netball shooting practice. As well as working your muscles, this helps to prepare you mentally.

By the end of the warm-up you should be sweating lightly. Move on to the training activity as soon as possible.

Light jogging: a good start to the warm-up for any training session, and a good way to cool down.

2 THE TRAINING ACTIVITY

This is the body of the training session. It could be:
◎ continuous, fartlek, circuit, weights or interval training
◎ an actual practice game, for example netball or football
◎ a skills training activity, e.g. a typical session for a cricketer might be:

Activity		Time (minutes)
batting	working on the different shots, a few minutes on each – off-drives, on-drives, pulls and cuts	15
fielding	close catching, high catching, picking up and throwing	15

3 THE COOL-DOWN

The **cool-down** is where you help your body to recover after vigorous exercise. It is just as important as the warm-up.

◎ Start with a few minutes of gentle exercise such as jogging. This helps to keep your circulation going. So more oxygen reaches your muscles and lactic acid is cleared away faster. This means less soreness.

◎ Finish with some stretching. This will help loosen your muscles and prevent stiffness. After heavy exercise muscles often get very tight.

Stretch those muscles. As part of the warm-up it helps to prevent injury. Do it in the cool-down to stop soreness.

RECOVERY RATE

Your recovery rate is how quickly your body gets back to normal after exercise. These are some of the changes that take place.

Heart rate. This slows down to your normal resting rate. How long it takes depends on how hard you exercise and how fit you are. The fitter you are the faster it returns to normal. It may take just a few minutes.

Lactic acid. Lactic acid is removed by oxygen when you repay the oxygen debt (page 30). It is removed faster when you do a cool-down (active recovery), as the graph on the left below shows.

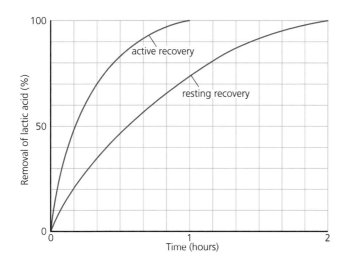

Glycogen stores. During exercise, muscle glycogen gets used up. It takes time to replace. After prolonged exercise such as marathon running, it can take 48 hours for glycogen stores to fully recover. Look at the graph on the right above.

Muscles. Your body has to repair any damage done to muscles during training. Stiffness and soreness take time to clear.

RECOVERY TIME

◎ Make sure you take enough time to recover between training sessions – 24 to 48 hours in the early stage of a training programme.
◎ If you train every day, follow a heavy session one day with a light session the next, to help recovery.
◎ Even during a heavy training period, take one rest day a week.

QUESTIONS

1 Describe the way a warm-up helps you.
2 Describe the way a cool-down helps you.
3 Look at the first graph above. **a** What does it show?
   b How long does the process take:
   i without an active cool-down? **ii** with an active cool-down?

Discussion work

4 You are doing an interval session involving reps of 20 metre sprints with a 10 second recovery between each. Discuss why you could manage about 10 reps if you did an active recovery, but only about 8 if you just stood still.

3.3   YOUR PERSONAL EXERCISE PROGRAMME

• • • • In this unit you will learn to plan your own personal exercise programme (PEP).

1 WHAT ARE YOUR NEEDS?

Jot down in the first page of your training diary the answers to the following questions.
◎ Your age.
◎ Your level of health – any recent illness, asthma, etc.
◎ Your current level of fitness – write down what you do in an average week using FITT.
◎ Why you want to be fitter.
◎ Exercise (or things about it) you enjoy/dislike.

MY PEP
My training needs
Age 15
Health . . .
Current fitness . . .

2 ANALYSE YOUR NEEDS

◎ What areas of fitness do you need to improve?
◎ What energy systems to you need to work on?
◎ What groups of muscles do you need?
◎ Will you need pressure training?

3 PLAN THE PROGRAMME

Plan the programme using principles of training. Start by doing one week and filling in anything you do regularly. Below in red is Dale's from page 41.

Monday –   Rest day
Tuesday –   Skills and sprint work at local club
Wednesday –   School match
Thursday –   fartlek, circuit or interval
Friday –   Rest day
Saturday –   Match
Sunday –   Match

His new work is in black. Dale should keep to this for several weeks until his body adapts.

Aerobic or stamina work for games players is usually done out of season because once you have reached a good level you can maintain it by playing lots of matches and doing the training above.

A SIX-WEEK PROGRAMME

Once you have the basic plan of your week you can then sketch out a six-week programme. Try to vary it to prevent boredom. Remember if you are unfit you will improve rapidly. Very fit people only make marginal improvements despite a whole season of training. This is why in sports such as the 100m sprint, world records get broken by only 100ths of a second. Unfit people may improve their time by five whole seconds!

Week		Session activity (time in minutes)
1	1	Swim 10 easy pace, full recovery. Repeat three times.
	2	Cycle 20, easy pace.
	3	Walk fast to school/college/town/work – 20.
2	1	Swim over the next few weeks, try to extend swimming time and reduce the rest until able to do a full 20 minutes.
	2	Cycle easy pace 20.
	3	Walk 20 fast or do another swim or cycle.
3	1	Swim 15, full recovery, swim 10, easy pace.
	2	Cycle 8 easy, 8 faster, 8 easy.
	3	Aerobics.
4	1	Swim 7 easy, two lengths faster, two lengths easy. Repeat until 15 minutes completed. Easy swim 10.
	2	Find a cycle route that takes approx 25 minutes of the old pace. Try to do it faster than this.
	3	30 minutes fast walk.
5	1	20 minutes easy swim. No rest!
	2	Repeat last week's cycle. Record time.
	3	Aerobics.
6	1	Swim 7 easy pace, 7 hard, 7 easy
	2	30 minutes cycle.
	3	Aerobics, walk, cycle or swim – minimum 20–30.

Remember Jane likes swimming. She is unfit and wants to lose weight. She *hates* jogging. Jane needs to do a minimum of three lots of 20 minutes weekly but at the moment she cannot do 20 minutes in one go. She needs to progress to this and exercise in moderation as too much causes pain and could put her off. In week one, Jane is really checking how much she can do and how she feels the next day. She did do 30 minutes of swimming but with rests in between.

Don't forget to keep a diary of how you feel. This will help you to know when to overload. Only work out detailed training for one week at a time as illness or other commitments may force a change.

QUESTIONS

1 Why do you think for a person like Jane it is better to increase time and intensity rather than frequency?

2 In Jane's cycling programme give examples of **a** how her intensity of training was overloaded. **b** how the timing of her sessions was increased.

3 If by week six Jane could complete that week's training comfortably, explain how you would overload her schedule for the following week.

Discussion work

4 When analysing needs you should know about the person's weight. Discuss if you think it is possible for a top-level performer to be overweight but not over-fat and if you think that this is a danger.

3.4 EXERCISE YOU CAN DO

In this unit you will learn how to choose the correct activities for your fitness level.

UNFIT PERFORMER

If, like Jane, you need to build up gradually you can do like she did with the swimming and apply the same principles to any other types of continuous training, e.g. cycling, rowing, or using aerobic machines in a gym. You will also gain benefits in muscular endurance, strength and provided you warm up correctly, also in flexibility. The aim is still the same – try to be out of breath for 20 continuous minutes then build up to 30.

AVERAGE PERFORMER

If you feel you are already quite fit (perhaps due to an active/busy lifestyle) and you want to be fitter you could do many different things. If your general fitness is OK (cardiovascular strength, flexibility, muscular endurance and strength) then you could do most other types of training without harm. You really need to be specific – why do you want to be fitter? If it is for general health, then continuous training methods – as above – are still very good. You should be able to train 5 times a week but may still need to build up to it. Include fun activities – if you are a social person – sports centres run aerobics and circuits. If you prefer working alone many have gyms where young people can use the aerobic machines, e.g. steppers and cross trainers. You can design a circuit based on body weight to do in your own home.

If you have decided that you want to be fitter for a certain sport then think about what areas of fitness your sport needs, e.g. water polo – requires strength, speed, agility, good reactions, flexibility, stamina, co-ordination – in other words EVERYTHING! Your training programme needs to reflect this. If you are playing water polo you probably belong to a club so train with them for skills at least once a week. A good circuit will help with strength, speed and agility and interval training will help your energy system and the necessary muscles for your sport.

Week 1 Session
1   Interval session in pool. Sprint half length swim to end. Repeat 10 times. Rest until heart rate is back to normal. This is one set. Do 3 sets if you feel ok.
2   Continuous training for 20–30 minutes.
3   Skill session with club.
4   Circuit session.
5   Match.

The good thing about the week's session above is that it is easily overloaded. The circuit will naturally overload as you get fitter and do more repetitions each week. The interval can have less or more repetitions, more sets or less rest. Vary to prevent boredom by changing the type of continuous training, or do aerobics instead occasionally. Try fartlek training occasionally – remember you can do it in a pool or by running and cycling. Remember to have an easy day following a hard one.

Continuous training.

Aerobic machines in a gym are fun and safe.

Water polo requires most areas of fitness – general and specific.

FIT PERFORMER

If you are very fit and seriously training then you should be able to put up with high heart rates. Do not be tempted to try to use weight training or long distance road running until you are fully grown.

More than one session can be done a day with a rest in between. With a high level of motivation you should be able to tolerate (put up with) high levels of lactic acid as top-level performance will require this. You must *always* have a weekly rest day and again try to have an easy day after a hard one. Here is an example based on netball:

Day	Activities/sessions
Mon	20–30 minute run. Weights: power session.
Tue	Sprint/circuit/interval session.
Wed	20 minute fast run. Skills training at club.
Thu	30–40 minute run.
Fri	Rest.
Sat	Match.
Sun	Weights. 20 minute fast run.

Progression, as with the last programme, should be obvious by applying overload.

LONG-DISTANCE TRAINING

If your sport involves lots of different areas of fitness it is easier to prevent boredom. But what about if you are a long-distance sportsperson? For events like these you can either do shorter work with greater effort or longer than normal but easier. For example, here is a week's training for an adult, one month prior to a 10-kilometre race:

Week 6	Session	Activity
	1	40 minutes with 6 × 1 minute hard with 1 minute rest.
	2	75 minute run.
	3	Rest.
	4	40 minutes with 5 × 30 seconds hard with 30 seconds rest.
	5	45 minutes easy.
	6	Rest.
	7	50 minutes run.

The New Zealand netball team practising skills.

QUESTIONS

1 If you were training for horse riding because you decided to take it up seriously, what areas of fitness would you concentrate upon?

2 Imagine that you have the opportunity to play a lot of golf because your parents work on a course. You play every day and are very good, but do no other sport. You decide that you are going to start fitness training. What areas do you think you should work on and why?

3 With your teacher's help it is now time to plan a PEP for yourself. Draw out your own six-week guide with a similar layout to Jane's.

Discussion work

4 Look up information on how bones grow and then discuss why you think you should not weight train or long distance road run until you are well-developed, or fully grown.

3.5 THE ATHLETE'S YEAR

• • • • In this unit you will learn how to peak at specific times of the year.

If you do judo, you can take part in judo events all year round. But many sports are **seasonal**. Cricket is an example. In the UK, cricket is played from April to September.

This shows how the year is divided for an athlete who plays a seasonal sport. The calendar is for a 'winter' sport such as netball or rugby. A cricket player will follow the same pattern but over different months, since cricket is a 'summer' sport. It is sometimes called **periodisation**.

June	July	Aug	Sept	Oct	Nov	Dec	Jan	Feb	Mar	April	May	June

1 PREPARATION	2 COMPETITION	3 RECUPERATION
(i) out-of-season / (ii) pre-season		

1 PREPARATION

i Out-of-season Here the athletes build up to a high level of general fitness. They do continuous training over long distances to improve aerobic fitness. They have strength training for the major muscle groups. They are careful with diet: lots of carbohydrate, not much fat!

This shows a typical out-of-season training programme for the England netball team:

Weekly programme for June/July	
Monday	4–5 mile run
Tuesday	Strength training using weights
Wednesday	3–4 mile run
Thursday	Strength training using weights
Friday	3 mile run
Saturday	Rest
Sunday	Strength training using weights

ii Pre-season Here the athletes focus on fitness for the sport. They run short fast lengths to improve anaerobic fitness and speed. They continue strength training on the muscles needed for the sport but work faster to improve their power.

Skills training becomes important, with circuits designed to practise different skills. For example footwork, shooting and defending in netball. Now is the time to really sharpen up.

Weekly programme for August/September	
Monday	Skills training including jumping (plyometrics)
Tuesday	3 mile run (time it and aim to go faster next time)
Wednesday	Strength/power training using weights
Thursday	Skills training including intense anaerobic work
Friday	Strength/power training using weights
Saturday	Fast 3 mile run
Sunday	Rest

2 COMPETITION

Here the athletes play at least two matches a week. The aim is to win! They still need training to maintain fitness, and to build up to their peak. The times of the season when you are at your fittest is called peaking. You aim to peak at the time of your biggest events. They need extra care to avoid injury at this time. It is easy to get injured through tiredness, or by overusing muscles.

Weekly programme for October	
Monday	Rest
Tuesday	Skills and weight training
Wednesday	Sprint or skills or plyometrics as necessary
Thursday	Fast 2 mile run, skills training
Friday	Strength/power training using weights
Saturday	Match
Sunday	Match

Many important events are overseas, in hotter weather or at higher altitude. The athletes will travel in advance so that they can train under the right conditions for the match.

3 RECUPERATION

Time for rest and relaxation. The aim is complete recovery from the competition season. But the athletes do not laze around. They play other sports for exercise and enjoyment. They are still careful with diet so as not to put on extra weight. Lots of carbohydrate, not much fat.

A happy and victorious Arsenal women's football team after winning the women's FA Cup.

QUESTIONS

1 Give three examples of: **a** seasonal sports **b** sports which are played all year round.

2 Look at the netballers' programme for June/July. What will be the effect of these activities?

3 The August/September programme includes some fast runs. Why?

Discussion work

4 In pairs choose a summer seasonal sport. Discuss and then sketch out how the year could be divided up to prepare for their sport. Sketch it out in the same manner as the one on the previous page.

QUESTIONS ON CHAPTER 3

1   If you were to devise a training programme what 3 steps do you need to take?

2   If you make the programme too hard what might happen?

3   Describe a warm-up you would do for either a rounders or a cricket game.

4   Why is an active recovery better than standing still?

5   Explain why you would be unable to run 2 marathons well if you were doing them on consecutive days.

6   This shows the first six weeks of a personal exercise programme designed for a woman aged 50. She hasn't done any exercise for months, but likes walking, so this is what she will be doing.

Week	1	2	3	4	5	6
Frequency	2	3	3	3	3	3
Time (min)	20	30	40	38	36	34
Distance (km)	1.5	2.3	3.1	3.1	3.1	3.1

   a   What is the correct technical name for this training method?

   b   Is it aerobic or anaerobic?

   c   How often does the woman walk in week two?

   d   From weeks three to six, the frequency and distance don't change. Does this mean there is no progression?

   e   What is the woman's maximum heart rate?

   f   What should her minimum heart rate be, during the walk, to ensure she is gaining aerobic benefit?

7   Joel is an 18-year-old tennis player.

   a   Why does he need to train regularly?

   b   Is 'once a week' regular training? Explain your answer.

   c   What would be the minimum weekly amount he would need to do to gain aerobic benefits?

   d   What does 'aerobic' mean?

   e   Name two sports that are mainly aerobic.

   f   What two other benefits of exercise may Joel gain as well as physical benefits? (Remember the definition of health.)

   g   Define the word 'fitness'.

   h   David Beckham is fit but so is David Smith in Year 11 who plays basketball (very badly!) three times a week. How can this statement be true.

8   Use the graph below, showing Joel's heart rate during a game of tennis, to answer the following questions.

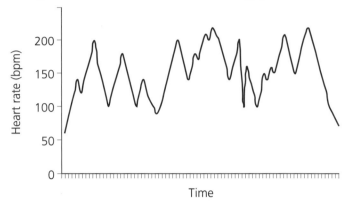

   a   Using the work 'threshold' explain why you think both aerobic and anaerobic work took place.

   b   What makes you think that Joel is fitter than the 'average' person?

   c   What is Joel's resting heart rate?

   d   What is the maximum it reaches?

   e   How do you work out a person's maximum heart rate?

   f   Joel has a quick recovery rate. What does this mean?

9   You are about to play a tennis match.

   a   Name two muscles you will use a lot during the match.

   b   What is the advantage of warming up these muscles before you start?

   c   What will you do to warm up your muscles?

   d   You should include stretching exercises in your warm-up session. Give two examples of how this will help you play a better game.

10 A very fit 16-year-old cross-country runner decides to overload their training and progresses to 6 miles a night around their local town. Is this a good training method?

11 A friend who is fairly unfit admires your level of fitness, why should you not encourage them to join in with your training schedule? Are there any parts of your schedule that would be suitable for them to do with you?

12

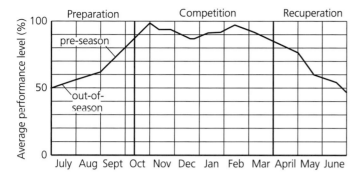

This graph shows how an athlete's level of performance changed through the year.

    a Her performance level improved all through the preparation period. Explain why.

    b It improved faster as she moved from out-of-season preparation to pre-season preparation. Why?

    c The athlete peaked (hit her top performance level) twice in the competition season. When did this happen?

    d There was a drop in performance in the second part of December. Why do you think this was?

    e The athlete's main event took place at the end of March. Was she at her best then?

    f Give reasons why an athlete's performance does not remain at its peak all through the competition season.

13 This shows a typical training programme for an 800m male runner during pre-season preparation:

Monday	50 min road run.
Tuesday	800 m on grass x 4 times, with a 3-minute rest between runs.
Wednesday	8 km run followed by weight training for arms, shoulders and legs.
Thursday	400 m run on track in around 62 secs. Repeat x 11 with a 2-minute rest between runs.
Friday	45 minute fartlek training.
Saturday	10 km easy run followed by weight training for arms, shoulders and legs.
Sunday	Rest day.

    a Give the correct name for the type of training he does:
      i On Mondays **ii** on Tuesdays and Thursdays.

    b What kind of fitness does the Monday session improve?

    c What kind of fitness is improved on Thursdays?

    d Give two examples of the type of activity he might do during fartlek training.

14 This graph shows time taken to clear lactic acid from the body after exercise.

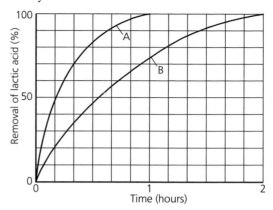

    a Why is it good to clear away lactic acid quickly?

    b One curve shows the time it takes to clear the lactic acid when the athlete does a cool-down. Which one?

    c Name one other benefit of the cool-down. Describe what activities you would do for a cool-down, after a hard game of tennis.

USE OF INFORMATION TECHNOLOGY

15 Devise an initial questionnaire for use in a sports centre to assess the needs of visitors who wish to start training. This should be an A4 sheet of paper, word processed with clear instructions on how it is to be completed.

APPLIED QUESTIONS

A16 Below the following questions will be the profiles of three people. You are now their fitness instructor.

    a Jot down the relevant information about each person (see page 44).

    b Write a brief analysis of their needs (see page 44).

    c Plan their first week's training with you.

    d Write a brief to explain this schedule to them.

Omar is 18. He is at school, studying A levels. He has played county level basketball for two years and has trials again soon. It is a month into his season. He is quite fit and is used to training every day. He has fully recovered from his ankle injury and his weight is normal.

Darren is 24. He is a professional athlete and runs the 100 metres. He has recently represented England for the first time. He is at optimum weight and has no injuries. In five weeks time there is an important race where he hopes to run an Olympic-qualifying time.

Jemma is 28. She has competed many times for England as a marathon runner. She trains full time but has missed two months of her normal training due to a stress fracture in her foot. She has now done two weeks of pain-free gentle running on a treadmill. She is slightly underweight.

4.1 THE FOOD YOUR BODY NEEDS

● ● ● ● In this unit you will learn the nutrients in food and their importance to exercise.

For energy, and to grow and repair itself, your body needs water and fibre and **nutrients**: carbohydrates, proteins, fats, vitamins and minerals.

CARBOHYDRATES

Carbohydrates are used for energy. They are broken down to **glucose** in your gut and used as a fuel for cell respiration (page 112). Some glucose is stored as glycogen in the liver and muscles.

Carbohydrates are found in sweet and starchy foods. Examples are bananas and other fruits, bread, biscuits, breakfast cereals, rice, potatoes and pasta. People training every day should have a high energy intake with 60% carbohydrate. Starchy carbohydrate is longer lasting.

These are just some of the foods that are rich in carbohydrates.

FATS

Fats are also used for energy. Muscles use a mixture of fats and glycogen. The mixture depends on how intense the exercise is, how long it lasts and how fit you are. For example:
◎ on a long walk, muscles use mainly fat
◎ start jogging and they'll start using more glycogen
◎ switch to a sprint and they'll use glycogen only
◎ jog for a few hours and they'll switch increasingly to fat, as glycogen gets used up
◎ the fitter you are, the more your muscles will use fat not glycogen.

Butter, margarine, and cooking oils are fats. Hamburgers, red meats, sausages, bacon, cheese and cream contain a lot of fat. So do oily fish, nuts and avocado pears. Fats are used in making crisps, cakes and biscuits.

These are all rich in fats.

PROTEIN

Your body needs protein to build cells, to make blood, and to restore and repair muscle and other tissues. They are found in meat, liver, chicken, eggs, fish, beans, peas, lentils and nuts. Your body can also use proteins for energy. But it will do this only if it has run out of carbohydrates and fats.

Some people believe that a high protein intake will make your muscles bigger and help you recover after training. However in western societies we already eat twice as much protein as we need. Excess protein leads to kidney problems and makes joints more susceptible to injury.

VITAMINS AND MINERALS

Your body needs tiny amounts of vitamins. Vitamins A and D can be stored in your liver. Vitamin C can't be stored. If you eat more of it than you need, the extra is excreted. That means you must eat it regularly. Minerals are just as important as vitamins. There is enough iron inside you to make a large nail. Without iron your blood can't carry oxygen. Without calcium you'd have no bones, teeth or muscle contractions.

These are rich in protein.

Substance	Where you find it . . .	Why you need it . . .	A shortage leads to . . .
vitamin A	fish, liver, vegetables, eggs, milk	to see in dim light and for healthy skin	night blindness and flaking skin
vitamin C	oranges and other citrus fruits, vegetables	for healthy skin and gums and to help wounds heal	scurvy
vitamin D	made by skin in sunshine; found in milk, fish, liver and eggs	for strong bones and teeth (you can't absorb calcium without it)	rickets
calcium	milk, cheese, dried fish, sardines, green vegetables	for strong bones and teeth, and for muscle contractions	fragile bones
iron	liver, beans, lentils, green vegetables; added to bread	for the haemoglobin in red blood cells	tiredness and anaemia
iodine	seafood and vegetables grown near the sea	for thyroid hormones that control the rate at which you burn up food for energy	a swollen thyroid gland (goitre)

WATER

Water does not give you energy. But around half your weight is water. Some is in your blood and other body fluids. Most is in your body cells, where it plays a vital part in reactions.

You could last for several weeks without food, but only 4 or 5 days without water. Once the level in your blood and body fluids falls too low, water is drawn out from the cells. You dehydrate and could die. You should drink at least eight glasses of water a day. If you play sports you may need to drink much more. Why?

FIBRE

Fibre is a substance called **cellulose** from the cell walls of plants. You find it in fruit, vegetables, brown bread, bran and other cereals. You can't digest it. It passes straight through the gut and is excreted as faeces. But it is very important because:

◎ it makes a bulky mass which your gut muscles can grip and push along quickly. This prevents constipation and bowel cancer.
◎ it absorbs poisonous wastes from digested food.
◎ it makes you feel full, so you eat less.

These will provide you with plenty of fibre.

QUESTIONS

1 If you have a big match/race at midday what sort of things should you have for breakfast and why?

2 What energy source (what nutrient) would you mainly use for marathon running?

3 If you came from a country where the diet was mainly rice what might you need to eat more of to help in a heavy training programme and why?

4 Why don't we have to do this in most European countries?

Discussion work

5 Discuss, one at a time, the extent to which a shortage of each vitamin and mineral will cause you to have a poorer sporting performance.

4.2   A BALANCED DIET

In this unit you will learn what is meant by a balanced diet.

YOUR ENERGY NEEDS

Even when you are relaxed and resting you need energy.
You need it to keep you warm, to keep your heart beating and lungs breathing, and for all the reactions that go on in your cells.

◎ Your **basal metabolic rate** (BMR) is the amount of energy you need just to stay alive, awake and comfortably warm.

◎ To move around, digest food and do exercise, you need even more energy. This is called **working energy**. It depends on how active you are.

◎ **total energy needed = basal metabolic rate + working energy**

It can be measured in **kilojoules** (kJ) or in **kilocalories** (C).
1 kilocalorie = 4.18 kilojoules

DIFFERENT PEOPLE HAVE DIFFERENT ENERGY NEEDS

Look at the table on the right. It shows how different people have different energy needs. It depends on:

◎ **your age.** You need more energy now than when you were little but as you get over the age of 40 your metabolism slows down and you need to eat less or you will gain weight.

◎ **your sex.** Males usually need more energy than females of the same age.

◎ **your lifestyle.** The more active you are, the more energy you need.

Total energy needed in a day (kJ)		
	male	female
child aged 8	8200	7300
teenager aged 15	11 500	8800
adult doing office work	10 500	9000
adult doing heavy work	14 000	10 500
a retired person of 75	9000	7000

HOW MUCH ENERGY DO FOODS GIVE?

Your body can use carbohydrates, fats and proteins for energy. Compare the energy each gives:

1 gram of carbohydrate	17.1 kJ
1 gram of protein	18.2 kJ
1 gram of fat	38.9 kJ

A gram of fat gives over twice as much energy as a gram of protein or carbohydrate. So it is very easy to eat much more fat than you need for energy. When this happens you put on weight!

Most foods are a mixture of carbohydrates, fats and proteins. Labels on tins and cartons often show what is in food and how much energy it will give you. Look at labels to find out what you are eating!

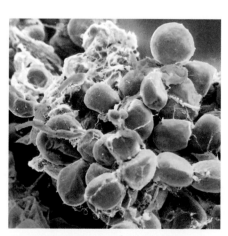

The yellow blobs are fat-storing cells, magnified by 150. Most of your fat-storing cells are laid down when you're a baby. When you eat more food than you need, they get bigger and you get fatter!

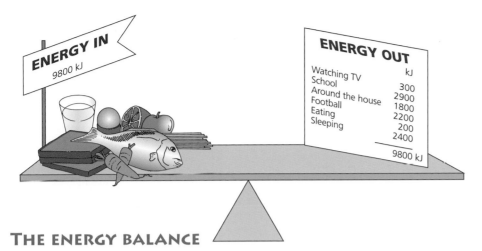

ENERGY IN
9800 kJ

ENERGY OUT	
	kJ
Watching TV	300
School	2900
Around the house	1800
Football	2200
Eating	200
Sleeping	2400
	9800 kJ

Energy in balance: if energy in = energy out you won't put on weight.

THE ENERGY BALANCE

Suppose you need 10 000 kJ of energy a day. You eat enough food to give 15 000 kJ. This is much more than you need. But the extra food is not excreted. Instead it is stored as fat. Even carbohydrate and protein are changed into fat and stored.

◎ If energy in is greater than energy out, the extra food is stored as fat and you gain weight. If you gain too much you may become **obese**.

◎ If energy in = energy out, your weight will not change.

◎ If energy in is less than energy out, your body will use up stored body fat for the extra energy. You will grow slimmer. But if too much body fat gets used up you'll become **anorexic**.

A BALANCED DIET

To be healthy you need a balanced diet. That means a diet that matches your energy needs and gives the right mixture of nutrients and fibre. Here are some guidelines for you.

◎ If you have to lift your own body weight, for example jumping, you won't be building up a huge muscle mass in training so your build shouldn't require huge amounts of calories.

◎ If you are doing long-distance work then you need to have plenty of starchy carbohydrates.

◎ No athlete needs to eat fatty foods. Fat is made from excess carbohydrates.

◎ By eating a balanced diet you will get enough fat (for long-distance/time sports) enough carbohydrate (for anaerobic work) enough protein (repairs) and enough vitamins, etc.

◎ Cut down on salt, sugar, fatty and processed (ready to cook) meals.

◎ Eat plenty of fresh fruit and vegetables.

A balanced diet: around 15% protein, 30% fat and 55% carbohydrate. Not only are carbohydrates good for you, they are also comparatively cheap.

QUESTIONS

1 What is your **basal metabolic rate**?

2 Explain why a teenage male needs more energy than:

    a A retired male

    b A female teenager.

3 What two units are used to measure energy?

4 If you eat more food than you need for energy, what happens to the extra?

5 What is a balanced diet?

Discussion work

6 Research and then discuss the amount of calories expended in a whole match or competition from four contrasting activities. Explain why you think this is so.

4.3

WEIGHT CONTROL AND FITNESS

●●●● In this unit you will learn how to control weight through diet and exercise.

BODY WEIGHT

What weight are you? It will depend on:

◎ your height and frame size. The longer and thicker your bones the more you will weigh.
◎ how much muscle and fat you have. (Muscle weighs more than fat.)
◎ your gender. Males are usually heavier than females. Why?

Weight tables show what weight a person of your height should be. If you are more than this you are **overweight**. You have too much fat – or perhaps even too much muscle. More muscle than you need for your work or sport puts extra strain on the heart, joints and ligaments. (See page 16 for a reminder on body shapes)

FITNESS AND BODY COMPOSITION

You could be the right weight but very unfit. For example, you could have lots of fat and only small weak muscles. So **body composition** is a better indicator of fitness. It shows how much fat you have compared with muscle, bone and other tissue.

◎ If you are male, no more than 13 – 15% of your weight should be fat. If it is more you are **overfat**. If it's over 20% you are obese.
◎ If you are female, no more than 18 – 20% of your weight should be fat. If it is more you are overfat. If it's over 30% you are obese.

You need a certain amount of fat. It forms a protective cushion around the kidneys and other organs. The layer of fat under your skin keeps you warm and acts as a store of energy. But **obesity** means you have an abnormal proportion of fat. If you are overfat or obese, the extra weight puts a strain on the heart, muscles, bones and ligaments. Exercise becomes difficult or even dangerous. Obesity causes joint and back injuries, and leads to heart attacks, strokes, liver disease and other problems.

UNDERWEIGHT?

You are **underweight** if you are below the normal weight range for your height. You could be underweight and overfat at the same time. Exercise will make you feel weak and tired.

ANOREXIA

Some people go on harsh diets to lose weight. This is very dangerous. It can lead to **anorexia**. You don't eat enough carbohydrate, so your body uses stored fat for energy. Then it runs out of fat and starts using proteins. It takes these proteins from your body tissues. So your organs stop working properly. You may die. Related to anorexia is **bulimia**. Individuals will eat large amounts of food and then induce vomiting.

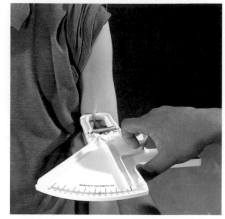

The skinfold test measures body fat. If you'd like to try it, ask your teacher.

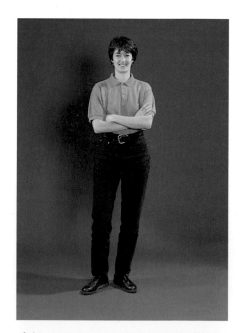

If this young woman were anorexic, she'd see herself as horribly obese. People with anorexia have a distorted self-image. They need both medical and emotional help.

HOW TO LOSE WEIGHT

The way to lose weight is by combining exercise and diet.

◎ Eat a healthy balanced diet and exercise more. Your body will use up stored fat to obtain the extra energy.
◎ Your muscles will grow when you exercise. Muscle weighs more than fat but takes up less space. So you won't lose much weight at the start but you will look slimmer.
◎ Regular exercise increases your basal metabolic rate. That means you use up more stored fat even when you are resting.
◎ Regular exercise reduces your appetite. You will find it easier to say no to food.

EATING FOR SPORT

The best food for sport is a healthy balanced diet.

◎ Don't eat more than you need. The extra will be stored as fat, and fat is a burden in sport.
◎ Carbohydrates will be your main source of energy. Remember, a balanced diet should contain at least 55% carbohydrate.
◎ You will also use fats for energy, depending on how intense the activity and how long it lasts. The more intense it is, the more you depend on carbohydrates. The longer it lasts, the more you depend on fats. But you don't need to eat extra fat. You have plenty stored.
◎ Intense exercise causes wear and tear to muscle and other tissue. Proteins are needed to repair the damage. But there's enough for that task in a normal diet. You don't need extra.
◎ Make sure you drink water during and after sport. Why?
◎ A balanced diet will give you enough vitamins and minerals. You do not need supplements. In fact an excess of vitamins A and D can be dangerous.

An athlete breakfasting before his big Olympic event. Plenty of carbohydrate!

Why do people say 'Don't swim straight after a meal'?
When you eat, a lot of your blood gets diverted from your muscles to your digestion system. This means that not a lot is available to carry oxygen to the working muscles. If you exercise, you will need to switch to anaerobic work sooner and will tire more quickly. This could be a big problem when swimming! You must be careful when eating a pre-match meal not to eat too close to the competition for the same reasons.

CARBOLOADING

For long events (two hours or more) athletes often use **carboloading**. First, cut down on carbohydrates and train hard. This uses up all your glycogen. Then eat lots of carbohydrates and train lightly in the days just before the event. Your muscles will now store more glycogen than usual.

By a combination of diet and exercise, some athletes have stored up to four times more glycogen than usual. But this can cause problems. Muscles may feel stiff and heavy. Kidneys may not function properly. The athlete may suffer chest pains. So a steady diet of at least 55% carbohydrate is a better solution.

QUESTIONS

1 What is *obesity*? What problems does it cause?
2 A person can be underweight *and* overfat. Explain.
3 Why are harsh diets dangerous?
4 List three ways exercise helps you lose weight.
5 What is *carboloading*? How does it help athletes?

6 You swim after a meal but find you tire quickly. Why might this be?

Discussion work

7 Discuss what your ideal meal would be the night before a competition and why.

4.4   DRUGS AND SPORT (1)

●●●● In the next two units you will learn the effects of drugs on your body.

DRUGS AND DOPING

A **drug** is any chemical substance you take that affects the way your body works. Most drugs were developed for medical purposes. They are dangerous when misused. **Doping** means taking drugs to improve sporting performance. It is a big problem in sports. Athletes take drugs for different reasons:

◎ to pep up their performance
◎ to kill pain so that they can keep going
◎ to build muscles faster than they can do by training
◎ to calm themselves before important events.

An athlete who dopes is cheating. The International Olympic Committee has drawn up a list of banned drugs. It includes the classes of drugs described below. International athletes can be tested for these drugs at any time, and face a ban of at least a year if the test is positive.

STIMULANTS

These stimulate the circulatory and nervous systems. They raise the heart rate and blood pressure, and speed up reactions. The person feels alert and confident, and can work hard for long periods without feeling pain or fatigue. Examples are:

◎ amphetamines, for example Dexedrine, Benzedrine, 'speed'.
◎ caffeine. This is a natural stimulant found in tea and coffee.

Stimulants are used in medicine to help patients with heart and lung problems. They are misused by athletes who want to improve their performance.

Dangers
◎ Pain and fatigue are the body's warning signals. If they are suppressed, the athlete carries on too long and risks cramps, strains, and overheating. Overheating can lead to heat stroke.
◎ When the stimulant has worn off the athlete feels really 'down'.
◎ Stimulants can cause violent and aggressive behaviour.
◎ Heavy use causes high blood pressure and liver and brain damage.

NARCOTIC ANALGESICS

These are pain-killers. **Narcotic** means causing drowsiness. **Analgesic** means killing pain. Narcotic analgesics act on the central nervous system and stop the body feeling pain. They give a feeling of well-being, relaxation and sleepiness. They include:

◎ morphine and heroin. These are used in hospitals to treat people in severe pain, for example cancer patients.
◎ codeine. This is a much milder drug. There is codeine in many of the pain killers and diarrhoea treatments on sale in chemist shops.

A dangerous drug? A caffeine level twenty times above 'normal' would get you banned from the Olympics.

Some athletes use narcotic analgesics to kill the pain from injury, so that they can carry on competing in events.

Dangers

◎ Narcotic analgesics cause constipation and low blood pressure.
◎ They cause extreme apathy.
◎ They are addictive. (Even codeine has its addicts.) The withdrawal symptoms can be very unpleasant.
◎ Carrying on in spite of injury will make the injury worse.
◎ Morphine and heroin are illegal in most countries except for medical use. In some countries, the punishment for being caught is death.

ANABOLIC STEROIDS

Anabolic steroids are hormones which help to build and repair muscle and bone. They occur naturally in the body. The male sex hormone testosterone is one example. They are also made artificially and used to treat people with wasting diseases. Some athletes and body builders take artificial steroids to increase the size and strength of their muscles and help them recover from training.

Dangers

If you take artificial anabolic steroids you stop the body making its own. This causes many problems, including:

◎ heart disease and high blood pressure
◎ weakened ligaments and tendons
◎ infertility and cancer
◎ aggressive behaviour
◎ the growth of facial hair, and deepening of the voice, in females.

DIURETICS

These increase the amount of water excreted in urine. They are used to treat patients with heart disease who have excess fluid in their bodies. They are misused by boxers and wrestlers who want to lose weight quickly before the weigh-in for a match, so that they get into the right group. They are also misused by athletes who drink lots of water to flush out traces of other banned drugs.

Dangers

◎ Essential sodium and potassium salts get eliminated as well as water.
◎ Low levels of potassium lead to muscle weakness and heart damage.

In the 2008 Beijing Olympic Games the followiing athletes were stripped of their medals:
• Lyudmila Blonska - silver, Heptathlon
• Kim Jong-su - silver and bronze, Pistol.
Another nine athletes tested poisitive. Blonska was banned for life as it was her second offence.

QUESTIONS

1 What is a **drug**?

2 What does **doping** mean?

3 Athletes who dope are cheats. Explain why.

4 Explain why International footballers at a World Cup somewhere hot, e.g. South Africa, might be in danger if they use stimulants.

5 Explain why a cyclist in the Tour de France might want to use a narcotic analgesic.

6 What are anabolic steroids? Give two reasons why throwers may use them.

7 What does a diuretic do?

8 Why might jockeys want to use diuretics?

Discussion work

9 For your best sport, discuss how drugs and doping might enhance performance. What particular dangers and disadvantages are there to taking these drugs?

4.5 DRUGS AND SPORT (2)

•••• DRUGS TO REDUCE ANXIETY

When you are anxious, the hormone adrenaline is released into your blood. It makes your heart beat faster and your palms sweat. It speeds up your breathing, and the conversion of glycogen to glucose in your muscles. You are ready for fight or flight.

Beta blockers block the effect of adrenaline. They slow down the heart and breathing. They are used in hospitals to treat patients with high blood pressure and heart disease. They are misused by athletes to calm their nerves before important events.

Beta blockers are banned in archery and shooting as well as some other sports. Can you explain why?

Dangers

◎ They can reduce blood pressure so much that the user faints.
◎ They lower performance during lengthy (endurance) events.
◎ They can cause sleeplessness, nightmares and depression.

Tranquillisers reduce anxiety and calm you down.
Examples are Librium and Valium.

Dangers

◎ They make the person feel dull and lacking in energy.
◎ They are addictive and can be very hard to give up.

BLOOD DOPING

Oxygen is carried in red blood cells. The more red cells you have, the more oxygen reaches the muscles. This helps them work for longer.

In **blood doping**, an athlete withdraws blood a few weeks before an important event. The red cells are separated and frozen. Just before the event they are thawed and injected back into the athlete.

Dangers

◎ All blood transfusions and injections carry a risk of infection.
◎ Top athletes already have a high concentration of red cells. Adding more may block their capillaries.

PEPTIDE HORMONES, MIMETICS AND ANALOGUES

Peptide hormones are naturally-occuring substances in our body that control certain functions. Analogues and mimetics are man-made drugs that mimic the hormones resulting in similar effects.

One of the most well known is EPO. This is the hormone that makes more red blood cells which would help in endurance events by carrying more oxygen to the muscles. It has the same dangers as blood doping.

Andreea Raducan a Romanian gymnast whose doctor gave her a cold remedy containing banned drugs. Her gold medal was taken away from her at the Sydney Olympic Games 2000.

Amongst other functions these hormones and drugs:

◎ increase muscle size and strength.
◎ help repair body tissue which promotes quicker recovery from injury and training.
◎ improve the blood's ability to carry oxygen by increasing the red blood cell count.

Dangers

◎ they can interfere with the normal hormone balance in the body
◎ allergic reactions
◎ high blood pressure
◎ diabetes
◎ abnormal growth of hands, feet and face; enlarged internal organs
◎ an abnormal increase in red blood cells carries the same dangers as blood doping.

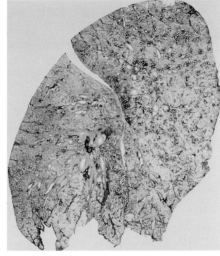

A section through a smoker's lung showing tar deposits. Imagine trying to breathe through that lot!

SOCIALLY ACCEPTABLE DRUGS

Nicotine and alcohol are socially acceptable drugs. But that does not mean they are good for you! Both of them lower your fitness.

Smoking

This is what you get in a cigarette:

◎ nicotine which is a poison. It is addictive. It makes your heart rate and blood pressure rise. It makes new smokers dizzy. It causes heart disease.
◎ tar, which is treacly brown stuff that collects in your lungs and respiratory system. It contains thousands of different chemicals. It clogs the lungs and stops you breathing properly. It causes lung cancer and bronchitis. Because it fills the alveoli with tar your lung volume is also reduced. This means you tire quicker.
◎ carbon monoxide, which is a poisonous gas in the smoke. In your lungs, red blood cells pick it up in place of oxygen. Less oxygen reaches your muscles and the rest of your body.

There is no 'safe' level of smoking. Every cigarette is dangerous. In the UK around 111 000 people a year die from diseases caused by smoking and around 2000 have legs amputated.

Alcohol

All alcoholic drinks contain a chemical called ethanol. It is what makes people drunk. It doesn't do much harm in small quantities. But larger quantities are dangerous.

◎ Alcohol affects co-ordination, judgement, balance, speech and hearing.
◎ It can make people aggressive.
◎ It causes the blood vessels of the skin to dilate, so you rapidly lose body heat. This can be fatal outside in cold weather.
◎ It lowers the level of glycogen in your muscles. This means they can't work so long or so hard.
◎ Athletes who drink too much lose their drive to train and compete.
◎ Long-term alcohol abuse leads to kidney and liver damage.

After heavy drinking, there will still be alcohol in the blood next day. Drinking alcohol the day before an important event is a very bad idea.

QUESTIONS

1 What two drugs might a snooker player use and why?
2 In theory, blood doping should improve an athlete's performance. Explain why.
3 Name the substance in cigarettes that causes the heart rate to increase.
4 Why would smoking a cigarette just before an endurance race affect your performance?

Discussion work

5 Discuss any sports person who has recently been caught taking drugs (you may need to research first). What were their initial gains, what health risks do they face and what was their punishment?

4.6 HYGIENE AND FOOT CARE

● ● ● ● In this unit you will learn how good hygiene helps prevent minor infections.

SWEATING

You have about three million sweat glands in your skin. During hard exercise in hot weather you can lose up to 3 litres of sweat an hour.

Sweat is water containing salts, ammonia and other wastes. It does not smell to start with, but the bacteria that live on your skin feed on it and produce smelly substances. It is important to shower and change your underclothes often to get rid of these smelly substances, and especially after exercise.

Deodorants and antiperspirants help you avoid sweaty smells. Deodorants mask the smell of sweat with a nicer smell. Antiperspirants coat the sweat pores with a film so the sweat can't get out. Since sweat helps you during sport, using an antiperspirant before a game is not a good idea.

CHOICE OF CLOTHING

Sports clothing must let you move freely. It must also let you sweat freely since sweat is your body's normal way to cool. Light loose cotton or cotton-polyester clothing is good for hot weather. Shorts and short-sleeved tops expose plenty of skin for sweat to evaporate.

In cold weather it is a good idea to wear several layers. The layers trap heat between them. You can then peel off layers as you get warmer. Cover your head and hands if it's very cold.

Remember, you sweat during exercise even in cold weather. Sports clothing should be washed frequently to remove sweat and bacteria.

Some of the bacteria that live on your skin and feed on sweat (magnified by 30 000). These are usually harmless. But if they multiply inside blocked pores you'll get a boil or pimple.

Clothes like these are fine for summer sports – but all-white clothes are even cooler!

FOOT INFECTIONS

Athlete's foot is a fungus that grows between your toes, making the skin cracked and itchy. It spreads from one person to another by direct contact, or you can pick it up from socks, towels and wet changing room floors.

To avoid athlete's foot, take care where you walk in your bare feet. Use flip-flops around swimming pools. Wash your feet often and dry them carefully between the toes. Avoid socks and shoes that make your feet sweaty. A fungus likes warm damp places!

Veruccas are flat warts that grow on the soles of your feet. They usually grow where your weight falls, so they can be painful. They are caused by a virus and they spread in the same way as athlete's foot. Veruccas are very contagious. If you have them, wear flip-flops in the changing room to stop them spreading!

To treat athletes foot you'll find sprays, powder and ointment in the chemist's. For verrucas you'll find ointments and medicated pads.

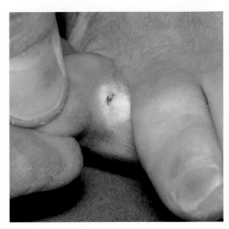

Watch out, there's athlete's foot about. It is highly contagious.

CORNS, BUNIONS AND BLISTERS

Shoes that are too tight can cause corns, bunions and blisters.

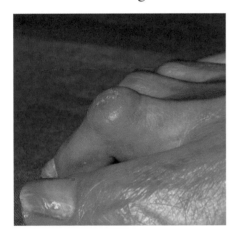

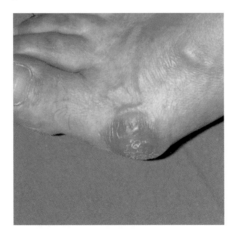

Corns are pads of thick hard skin that form on the toes and soles of feet. They can be very painful. Corn plasters may help, or go to a chiropodist.

At the joint of your big toe is a cushion of liquid called a *bursa*. If it gets inflamed the result is a *bunion*. If a bunion is very painful you will need surgery.

Friction causes skin to *blister*. Don't burst a blister. If it does burst keep it clean and dry and cover it with gauze. Don't pick off the scab that forms.

QUESTIONS

1 What makes sweat smell?
2 What does a deodorant do?
3 What does an antiperspirant do?
4 Why are shorts better than jogging bottoms for tennis on a hot day?
5 How would you know if you had athlete's foot?

Discussion work

6 You have gone into a shop and bought some trainers half a size too small because they are massively on offer and look great! Discuss the problems that could occur and how these could affect your performance in sport.

4.7   RISK ASSESSMENT

• • • • • In this unit you will learn the risks you face when doing sporting activities and how to reduce the chance of potential accidents and injuries.

Before doing sport, especially if you are the coach or the leader, you should do a **risk assessment** to try to reduce the risk of injury as much as possible. You can never completely prevent it but you can minimise the dangers.

RISK ASSESSMENT

There is no set layout for a risk assessment form but you should take the following steps:
◎ Identify the hazard(s).
◎ Identify who could be at risk and how.
◎ Note down how the risks could be minimised.
◎ Review on a regular basis and update.

An example of a typical form:

Weight categories help to reduce the risk of injury due to different physiques

Risk assessment
Club_____ Club leader _____
Date_____

Hazard	Who is at risk	Control measures (to reduce risks)	Further control measures (i.e. after reviewing)

The following risks are all areas you should consider and most of them we have already covered in detail.

1 Poor or incorrect fitness
The best way to prevent injury is be fit for your activity. For example, you shouldn't attempt to hold up a scrum in rugby without good neck strength. If you are feeling ill or recovering from injury you should not take part in an event. If you overdid it in a stamina sport you may have to give up before the end. This may make you feel like you failed.

Being active is safe for most people but there are some who might need to get medical advice before choosing a suitable type of activity. Filling out a PAR-Q (Physical Activity Readiness Questionnaire) is sensible for those over the age of fifteen. Many versions can be downloaded from the internet, all ask a series of questions about your health, for example: Do you get pains in your chest? If the answer to any is 'yes' you should see your doctor for advice before starting activity.

2 Incorrect physique
In 1.6 we looked at physique. Some sports require a certain physique to be safe, e.g. a heavy mesomorph or endomorph shouldn't do jumping activities such as triple jump, or a lot of running on hard surfaces as they will risk joint injuries. In many contact sports, boxing for example, there are weight categories and most children's sports have age groups to help match physique and skill.

3 Incorrect technique/skill
A good coach with recognised qualifications is needed to prevent poor technique and long term injury that could otherwise be caused. Repetitive action sports, for example tennis, contact sports and ones using maximum effort, are most at risk.

4 Poor behaviour

Know the rules for your sport and obey them. Rules were developed to protect players as well as to test their skill.

5 Incorrect clothing and personal equipment

Make sure you are wearing the right kit. Wear light or warm clothing depending on the weather. If your sport requires protective gear such as gum shields or shin pads, make sure you wear it. The correct footwear is especially important. Many injuries are due to poor footwear as the weight going through your feet can be enormous! Well-cushioned shoes protect your knees and back as they absorb impact. Make sure that rugby boots, etc., have no loose studs.

If you have long hair, tie it back. Do not wear a watch or jewellery that could catch in equipment or clothing. For sports such as wrestling and netball you must keep your fingernails short.

6 Damaged or inappropriate equipment

Make sure the equipment you use is safe. For example, that wooden equipment such as bats have no splinters and that gymnastics mats are not worn thin in places. Use mini rackets, etc., where appropriate. Use foam balls or soft equipment when appropriate. Check for vandalism where appropriate.

7 Poor lifting and carrying technique

If you lift equipment the wrong way – for example, gymnastics equipment or trampoline wings – you may find yourself injured before you even start! Keep your back straight and use your legs.

8 Unsafe environment

There are two main dangers, the *surroundings* and *weather*.

Watch out for hazards in the playing and changing areas, such as broken glass on pitches, wet patches on floors, or rakes left lying in long jump pits. Be aware that roads may need crossing from changing areas to the fields/courts, etc.
The weather can also be a hazard. Frost can make ground too hard. High winds and fog are hazards for canoeists, windsurfers and sailors.

9 Not preparing properly

Warm up and cool down correctly. Many injuries such as sprains and pulled muscles can be avoided by warming up correctly. In cold weather wear a tracksuit and plenty of layers. We looked at this in detail in unit 3.2.

10 Poor diet

Your body needs nutrients or energy to grow and repair itself. A lack of these can cause fatigue, poor performance and a weakness of the bones or muscles. These could cause poor concentration, accidents and injury. We looked at this area in more detail in unit 4.1.

11 Taking drugs

A drug is any chemical substance you take that affects the way your body works. Most drugs were developed for medical purposes and are dangerous when misused.

As you know from earlier in the chapter using unauthorised drugs means you not only risk your health but also face the risk of a ban.

QUESTIONS

1 List three sporting activities that could result in injury to certain physiques.

2 Name a repetitive action sport apart from tennis. Why could the wrong technique in this lead to over-use injuries fairly quickly compared to other sports?

3 Choose one of your main sports. Write down how the risks in this unit relate to it.

4 You are running a year 8 inter-form netball competition at 4pm in November outside. The posts are stored outside the court area. What risks do you feel are potential dangers and how would you minimise them?

Discussion work

5 Poor diet can result in a lack of concentration. Discuss in at least three varied sports how this can lead to injury.

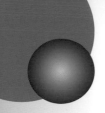

QUESTIONS ON CHAPTER 4

1 Which statement is not true?
  A Vitamin C is needed for healthy gums.
  B A gram of fat gives over twice as much energy as a gram of protein.
  C Vitamins give you energy.
  D Calcium, iodine and iron are minerals.

2 Match each substance i–v below to one of the statements A to E.
  A helps move food through your gut faster
  B your blood could not carry oxygen without it
  C the body's first choice for energy
  D is found in every cell in your body
  E needed for the hormones that control how fast you burn up food
  i water   ii carbohydrates
  iii iodine   iv fibre
  v iron

3 Name two foods you could eat to obtain each substance:
  a carbohydrate   b vitamin C
  c protein   d fibre
  e fat   f vitamin A

4 a What is *basal metabolic rate*?
  b Why do you need energy even when you are lying down perfectly still?
  c The bigger you are, the bigger your basal metabolic rate is. See if you can explain why.

5 Arrange these in order of how much they need to eat. The person who needs to eat least should come first:
      a male student of 17
      a retired woman of 75
      a coal miner of 40
      a boy of 12
      a female student of 17

6 a What is a *healthy balanced diet*?
  b What proportion of carbohydrates, fats and proteins should you eat for a healthy balanced diet?
  c Write down six guidelines for a healthy balanced diet.
  d Grilling is a healthier way than frying to cook fish and meat. Explain why.
  e Give three examples of processed foods.
  f What are food additives?
  g A diet of only processed foods is unhealthy. Explain why.

7 Say whether each statement below is true or false.
  a You should take 55% of your carbohydrate in the form of sugar.
  b If you need more energy than your diet provides, the extra is obtained from stored fat.
  c Potatoes provide you with vitamin C.

  d You need more vitamins and minerals when you are training hard.
  e Lean meat is high in fibre.

8 1 kilogram of stored body fat = 32 000 kJ. Suppose your energy needs are 10 000 kJ per day, and you eat enough food to provide 14 000 kJ per day.
  a How much more energy do you take in per day than you need?
  b Are you eating too much food for your needs, or too little?
  c What happens to this extra food?
  d At this rate, how long would it take you to gain an extra kilogram in weight?

9 A small tin of baked beans contains:

protein	9.6g	fat	0.4g
carbohydrate	27.9g	fibre	7.6g
salt	2.5g	energy	640kJ

  a Baked beans are a good source of fibre. Why is fibre good for you?
  b You should eat around 18g of fibre a day. What could you eat with baked beans to provide more fibre?
  c You should eat no more than 1.6g of salt a day. Why is too much salt harmful?
  d What advice would you give the makers of baked beans about the amount of salt they use?

10 A unit called the calorie is also used to measure the energy value of food. Labels will show both kilocalories and kilojoules. Copy and complete:
  a 1 kilocalorie = _____ calories
  b 1 kilocalorie = _____ kilojoules
  c 50 kilocalories = _____ kilojoules

11 Muscles can use both carbohydrate (glycogen) and fat for energy. As this bar graph shows, the extent to which your muscles depend on each source depends on the activity: Which is the main source of energy used in:
  a the Tour de France?
  b boxing (each round 3 minutes)?
  c resting?
  d a 20-minute jog?
  e the 100m sprint?

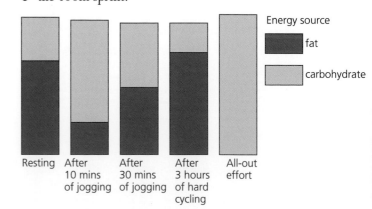

12 a Write down all the reasons you can think of why sports people should not use drugs.

b Which reason do you think is the most important?

13 Write down two harmful effects of using:

a stimulants

b anabolic steroids

c pain killers during exercise

14 a Which substance in alcohol makes you drunk?

b Write down three ways in which alcohol will affect a competitor's performance during a sports event.

15 a Cigarettes contain an addictive substance which is poisonous. What is it called?

b Cigarette packets carry the message 'Smoking can kill'. Name three ways in which smoking is harmful.

APPLIED QUESTIONS

Below are the four profiles used previously with some additional information.

Omar is 18. He is at school studying A levels. He has played county level basketball for two years and has trials again soon. It is a month into his season. He is quite fit and is used to training every day. He hasn't been injured, is 6'4" and weighs 166lbs.

Darren is 24. He is a professional athlete and runs the 100 metres. He has recently represented England for the first time. He is 6'2" and weighs 194lbs. He has no injuries. In five weeks time there is an important race where he hopes to run an Olympic-qualifying time.

Jemma is 28. She has competed many times for England as a marathon runner. She trains full time but has missed two months of her normal training due to a stress fracture in her foot. She has now done two weeks of pain free gentle running on a treadmill. She is 5'8" and weighs 118lbs.

Chloe (the rugby player from chapter 2) is 5'8" and weighs 155lbs.

A16 Explain the relevance of the following information about each athlete in relation to preparing properly for their sport:

a Omar doesn't like milk products (e.g. cheese) and hates fish. He tries to eat vegetables occasionally but does not like them.

b Darren is eating the correct amount of calories. Chloe eats the same amount as Darren.

c Jemma has to travel a long way for her club training and also has two children. She is very busy and sometimes misses out on meals.

d Chloe has 28 per cent body fat and is slightly overweight. Because of her rugby position she believes it is an advantage as she won't get tackled to the floor easily.

THINGS TO DO

A calculator will help for some of these.

A17 Before you do activities 19 – 21 you will need to:

a collect labels from at least one chocolate bar and one packet of crisps, showing how much energy they give.

b weigh yourself in kilograms.

A18 This table shows the amount of energy burned up per kilogram of body weight per minute, for different levels of activity.

Energy used in . . .	kJ per kilogram per minute
resting	0.13
moderate exercise (e.g. jogging or swimming)	0.59
vigorous exercise (e.g. football or netball)	0.79

a Calculate how much energy you burn up per minute when you are resting. (0.13 kJ × your weight)

b Calculate how much you burn up per minute during moderate exercise. (0.59 kJ × your weight)

c Calculate how much you burn up per minute during vigorous exercise. (0.79 kJ × your weight)

d Produce a spreadsheet using the above formulas where you can enter your weight and the number of minutes at each type of exercise and get a total energy usage.

A19 A Picnic bar provides 960kJ of energy. If you weigh 60kg, you burn up 7.8kJ of energy per minute when resting. So it will take you (960 ÷ 7.8) minutes to burn up the energy from the Picnic bar. That is 123 minutes, or 2 hours 3 minutes.

a Look at your chocolate bar label. How much energy does the bar provide?

b Work out how many minutes it would take you to use up this energy during vigorous exercise.

c Look at the crisps packet label. How much energy do the crisps provide?

d Work out how long it would take to work off this energy during moderate exercise.

A20 1 gram of stored body fat = 3.2kJ. If you do not burn off your chocolate bar, work out how much weight you will gain from it.

A21 Keep a record of everything you eat for one week.

a Try to work out what proportion of carbohydrates, fats and proteins you ate. (Labels on food packets will help you.)

b Estimate how much energy this food has provided. Then work out your average daily energy intake.

c Assume your energy needs are 11 000kJ if you are male and 9000kJ if you are female. Did you eat too much? Or too little?

d Did you eat a healthy balanced diet? Explain.

5.1 BONES

• • • • In this unit you will learn the names of the major bones and the importance of their composition to sport.

How tall will you be? Will you be petite or will you have thick, heavy bones? As mentioned in the previous section, bone/body size is an important factor in high-level sports. Bones don't stop growing completely until you are in your early twenties.

THE COMPOSITION OF A TYPICAL ADULT LONG BONE

The arm and leg bones of an adult look like this:

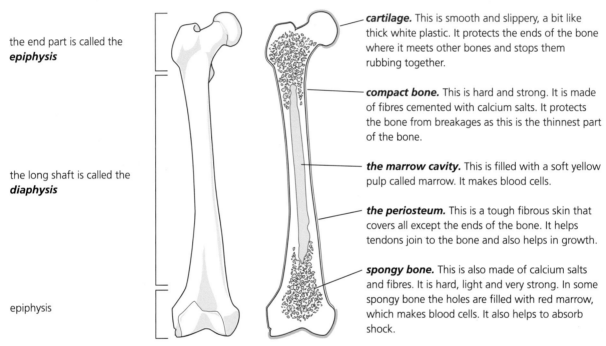

the end part is called the **epiphysis**

the long shaft is called the **diaphysis**

epiphysis

cartilage. This is smooth and slippery, a bit like thick white plastic. It protects the ends of the bone where it meets other bones and stops them rubbing together.

compact bone. This is hard and strong. It is made of fibres cemented with calcium salts. It protects the bone from breakages as this is the thinnest part of the bone.

the marrow cavity. This is filled with a soft yellow pulp called marrow. It makes blood cells.

the periosteum. This is a tough fibrous skin that covers all except the ends of the bone. It helps tendons join to the bone and also helps in growth.

spongy bone. This is also made of calcium salts and fibres. It is hard, light and very strong. In some spongy bone the holes are filled with red marrow, which makes blood cells. It also helps to absorb shock.

All the features of the bone above are vital to us in sport and all develop with training.

Cartilage. Imagine how our bones would rub together if we did not have cartilage. Exercise causes cartilage to become thicker, so our joints move smoothly and absorb shock better as we jump or run.

Compact bone. This becomes thicker as we train and exercise. This means we are better protected against impact injuries and thicker bones mean we can train with heavier weights.

Marrow cavity. This produces red and white blood cells. With regular exercise this process is speeded up. More blood cells means more blood, and this means more oxygen can be carried round the body. This in turn means more exercise can be performed.

Periosteum. One of the functions of the periosteum is to lay down bone cells so the bone grows in width. With exercise this process is increased so our bones are thicker and stronger.

Spongy bone. If our bones grow thicker we must also have more spongy bone. This helps with shock absorption and making more blood cells.

THE SKELETON

Without your skeleton you'd be just a shapeless sack of flesh. The skeleton has 206 bones, held together at **joints** by strong fibres called **ligaments**. These are its main bones:

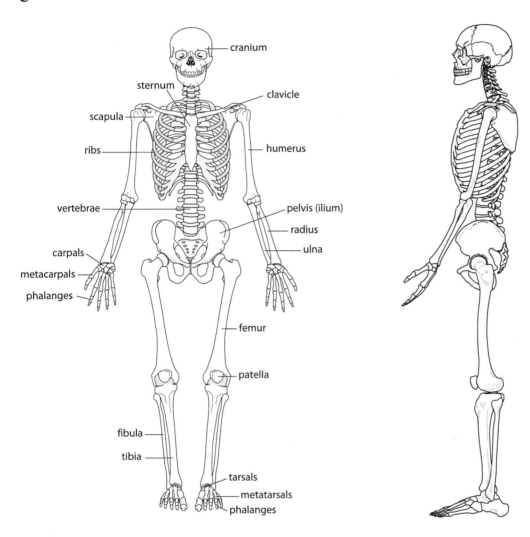

Each arm and leg has three long bones. Look at the bone sticking out at the end of the backbone, in the side view. It's the remains of a tail!

QUESTIONS

1 Without looking at the diagram, see if you can quickly sketch a typical long bone and put on all five labels.

2 Why should jockeys not do a vast amount of strength training?

3 Thicker bones mean we can lift heavier weights when training. What lays down bone cells to make the bone grow in width?

4 Why do American footballers and rugby players need thick strong bones?

5 Name the bones that make up the **a** knee joint **b** hip joint **c** shoulder joint

6 What do you think happens to bone if you are in hospital for a long time or do hardly any exercise?

Discussion work

7 Think of one of your major sports. How would the composition of your bones aid you in this activity?

5.2 THE FUNCTIONS OF THE SKELETON

• • • • In this unit you will learn the functions of the skeleton and the types of bone contained in it.

1 **Shape and support.** These two functions are similar. The bones form a framework to support your body just like steel girders in a building. The different length and thickness of the bones determine our individual shape and what sports we are most suitable for, although when playing for fun or at a low level it does not matter. Remember the information from the last chapter about this.

2 **Protection.** Bones surround the areas that are delicate and could get damaged. The vertebral bones surround our spinal cord, and our skull acts as an internal crash helmet to protect our brain. Our ribs and sternum act as a flexible but strong surround to protect lungs, heart, kidneys, etc.

3 **Movement.** Your muscles are firmly attached to your skeleton. Muscles work by contracting or getting shorter. When they contract they pull on bones. This makes the bones move. The longer the bones, the greater the range of movement possible. The shorter the bone, the easier it is to generate power.

4 **Blood production.** Bones make blood cells in the marrow cavity and spongy bone. These cells are then used to transport gases around the body.

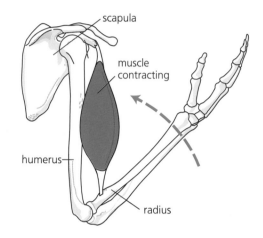

Bones move when muscles contract.

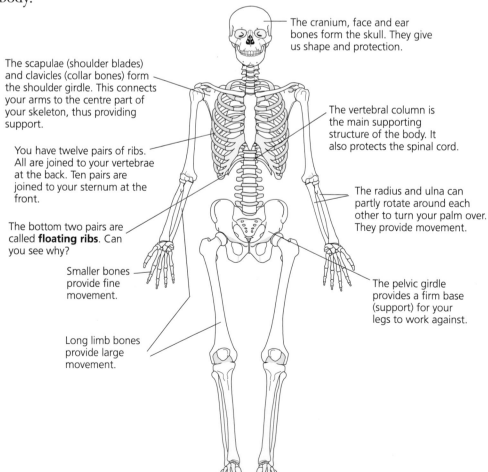

The cranium, face and ear bones form the skull. They give us shape and protection.

The scapulae (shoulder blades) and clavicles (collar bones) form the shoulder girdle. This connects your arms to the centre part of your skeleton, thus providing support.

You have twelve pairs of ribs. All are joined to your vertebrae at the back. Ten pairs are joined to your sternum at the front.

The bottom two pairs are called **floating ribs**. Can you see why?

Smaller bones provide fine movement.

Long limb bones provide large movement.

The vertebral column is the main supporting structure of the body. It also protects the spinal cord.

The radius and ulna can partly rotate around each other to turn your palm over. They provide movement.

The pelvic girdle provides a firm base (support) for your legs to work against.

THE FOUR TYPES OF BONES IN YOUR SKELETON

Your bones are different shapes and sizes because they have different jobs to do. They are divided into four groups:

1 **Long bones.** These are shaped like the bone shown in unit 5.1. They have a diaphysis, epiphyses and a hollow centre. Your height, shoe size and glove size depend on long bones.
Examples: the bones of the upper and lower arms and legs, the collar bone, the ribs, the metatarsals, metacarpals and phalanges.

2 **Short bones.** These are small and squat. They are spongy bone covered with a thin layer of compact bone. So they are light and very strong.
Examples: the carpals of the wrist, the tarsals of the feet.

3 **Flat bones.** These are spongy bone between two layers of compact bone. They have a large surface area.
Examples: the scapula, pelvis and cranium. The scapula and pelvis need a large area for all the muscles that attach to them. The cranium needs a large area to protect the brain.

4 **Irregular bones.** These are spongy bone inside and compact bone outside. They are specially shaped to suit the job they have to do.
Example: the vertebrae.

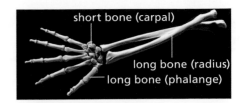
short bone (carpal)
long bone (radius)
long bone (phalange)

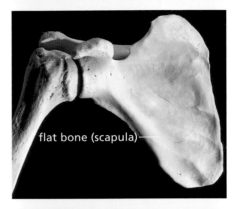
flat bone (scapula)

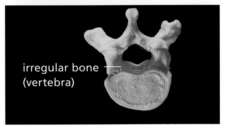
irregular bone (vertebra)

FUNCTIONS

◎ **Long bones.** These mainly act as levers for a large range of movement, e.g. the very long ones (radius, ulna and humerus) all work together to allow you to hit a shuttlecock a long way in badminton. The smaller long bones, e.g. phalanges and metacarpals, allow you to perform more delicate movements, like net shots. People who do sports where you need to impart momentum to things, often have long levers.

◎ **Short bones.** These provide movement where it is needed in lots of directions but also give strength.

◎ **Flat bones.** These protect delicate organs and give a big surface area for muscle attachment.

◎ **Irregular bones.** These protect for example the spinal cord, and provide support.

QUESTIONS

1 In some sports the bones alone cannot provide enough protection. Name three sports and some pieces of extra protective equipment that are used in them.

2 Apart from identical twins, all 58 million of us in Britain look different. Why?

3 Name two sports where it would be good to have long thin bones. Explain.

4 Name a sport where it would be good to have long thick bones. Explain.

5 Name a sport where it would be good to have short thick bones. Explain.

6 Are the following bones long, short, flat or irregular?
a radius **b** cranium **c** carpal **d** humerus **e** vertebra
f metatarsal **g** phalange **h** scapula.

Discussion work

7 Think of one of your major sports. Discuss how the skeletal functions help you perform it.

5.3 BONE GROWTH

• • • • In this unit you will learn how bones grow and the effects of exercise on them.

HOW BONES GROW

You do not need to know how bones grow but it helps you understand why you must be careful not to do certain types of exercise when young. Inside the womb, your bones start life as cartilage. Over the years this turns into bone in a process called ossification. Ossification is the development and growth of bone. This shows what happens:

4 weeks

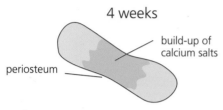

A periosteum grows round the cartilage. It will control the shape and thickness of the bone. Then calcium salts build up.

8 weeks

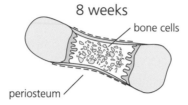

Bone cells appear in the middle. They start changing the cartilage into bone. The periosteum also lays down bone.

Birth

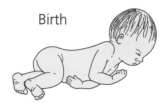

By the time you are born, bones are still mostly cartilage. They are quite soft and easily bent.

9 years

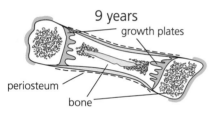

Next, bone cells appear at the ends and change these to bone. Two bands of cartilage remain. They are called **growth plates** or **EPIPHYSEAL PLATES**.

15 years

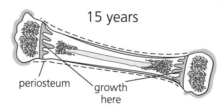

The plates grow at the outer edge so the bone gets longer. At the same time the inner edge is being turned into bone. The periosteum continues to lay down cells so the width grows slowly.

23 years

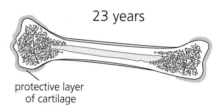

Growth stops when the plates are all bone. Now the only cartilage left in the bone is the thin layer at each end.

The whole process is controlled by hormones. If there is too much **growth hormone**, the cartilage in the plates grows too fast and the person could end up a giant. If there is too little the person fails to grow.

It is vital at these ages that children do not overdo certain kinds of exercise. Weight training, hard contact sports and long-distance road running could cause the bone – still cartilage in places – to grow unevenly, causing problems such as bow legs. It is equally important that exercise is done regularly to promote good bone growth.

DIET AND BONE GROWTH

Diet was discussed in chapter 4. The most important nutrients for growth are proteins, vitamins and minerals.
◎ Proteins build cells and repair damage.
◎ Vitamins help with things like absorbing calcium thus giving us strong bones and helping wounds heal.
◎ Minerals: there are many of these and they give us strong bones, help muscles contract and help control the rate we burn energy.
Vitamins and minerals cannot be stored in the body so we need a regular supply.

BONE CELLS AND EXERCISE

Even when a bone has stopped growing, it is full of life. Bone cells called **osteoblasts** make new bone and at the same time cells called **osteoclasts** break it down. Exercise causes osteoblasts to work harder and makes bones strong and thick.

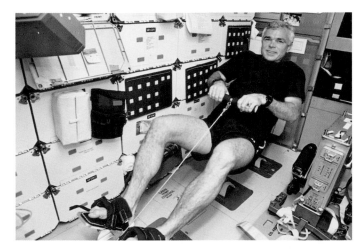

Press-ups get those osteoblasts going! But in space, weightlessness means both bones and muscles will weaken. So an exercise machine is part of the astronaut's space kit.

BONES AND AGEING

Bones get lighter as you age; exercising to make the osteoblasts work is vital. Men's bones tend to be thicker than women's and many older women suffer from osteoporosis, where bones get so weak they break easily. Gentle cardiovascular exercise (avoiding high impact) can help prevent this. It is very important to keep exercising when you get old.

OPTIMUM WEIGHT

We looked at the importance of bone size for specific sports in the last chapter. In some sports you may even want to develop and strengthen some bones but not others. Boxers do a lot of upper body strength work, thickening their arm bones, but do not want to do this to their legs. Can you think why?

Ideal weight for everyday life varies. An adult who is 1.7m tall could weigh anywhere between 57kg (small frame with small bones) and 76kg (big frame).

QUESTIONS

1 Name the skin-like substance that causes bone to grow in width.

2 Name the plates that cause it to grow in length.

3 Why is it correct for an adult to lift heavy weights repeatedly but not a child?

4 Name two other types of training that are bad for youngsters.

5 Name the three most important nutrients for bone growth.

6 The optimum weight for a person who is 1.7m tall can vary by up to 19 kilograms. How can this be?

7 If you were a marathon runner do you think it would be good to do lots of training to make your bones really strong and thick? Explain your answer.

Discussion work

8 Discuss what types of exercise you would recommend to an elderly person and why. What would be the benefits to them?

5.4   DIFFERENT KINDS OF JOINTS

• • • • • In this unit you will learn the types of joints in your body.

Your skeleton is made up of bones. **Joints are where two, or more, bones meet.** They are divided into three types depending on how freely the bones can move. If we did not have joints no movement could occur.

FIXED OR IMMOVEABLE JOINTS

The bones at an immoveable joint can't move at all. They interlock or overlap, and are held close together by tough fibre. The joints between the plates in the cranium are a good example. The fused joints in the sacrum are another example. We have this type of joint in areas requiring great strength.

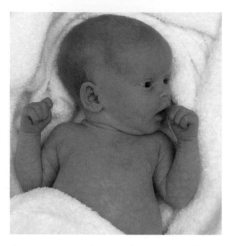

Gaps between plates in the cranium allow a baby's head to squash during birth. Twelve months later the gaps will have closed and fixed joints will have started to form. This strong joint will then almost completely protect the brain.

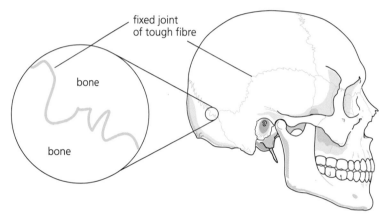

fixed joint of tough fibre

bone

bone

SLIGHTLY MOVEABLE JOINTS

The bones at a slightly moveable joint can move only a little. They are held together by strong white cords or straps called ligaments and joined by **cartilage**. This is like a gristly cushion. It stops the bones from knocking together. It can squash a little to let them move.

The joints between most of your vertebrae are slightly moveable. The pads of cartilage between them act as shock absorbers so the bones won't jar when you run and jump.

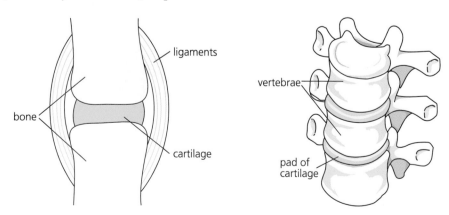

ligaments

bone

cartilage

vertebrae

pad of cartilage

The joints between your ribs and sternum are also slightly moveable. They move a little when you breathe in and out.

FREELY MOVEABLE JOINTS

At a freely moveable joint the bones can move quite freely. The knee joint is a good example.

A freely moveable joint has these parts:
◎ an outer sleeve called the **joint capsule**. This holds the bones together and protects the joint. It is an extension of the skin or periosteum that covers each bone.
◎ a **synovial membrane**. This lines the capsule and oozes a slippery liquid called synovial fluid.
◎ a **joint cavity**. This is the small gap between the bones. It is filled with synovial fluid. This lubricates the joint so that the bones can move more easily.
◎ a covering of smooth slippery **cartilage** on the ends of the bones. It stops the bones knocking together.
◎ **ligaments** which hold the bones together and keep them in place. Freely moveable joints are also called **synovial joints**. (Why?)

Most of your joints are synovial. Otherwise you couldn't move so easily! The elbow, shoulder, hip and finger joints are examples.

Before we look at types of synovial joints (Unit 5.6) we are going to look at types of movement (Unit 5.5). Knowing about these will help you to understand what is possible at each type of joint.

JOINTS AND INJURY

Joints can be damaged by general wear and tear or impact.
◎ Impact. Severe contact, e.g. falling from a horse onto your shoulder, could cause dislocation. This is where a bone is pulled out of its normal position at the joint. It would cause tearing of ligaments (sprain) and tendons. These would also tear with injuries such as going over on an ankle.
◎ Wear and tear. Exercise of a joint or an unusual use of it (perhaps due to another injury) could cause cartilage to be worn away. Just as in impact injuries, the joint would then swell causing it to stiffen – the body's way to tell you to stop moving it! In elderly people this wear and tear can cause arthritis. This makes the joint stiff and swollen.

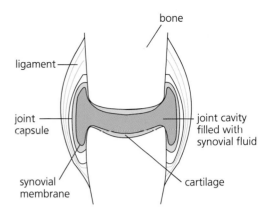

Knee joint from the back.

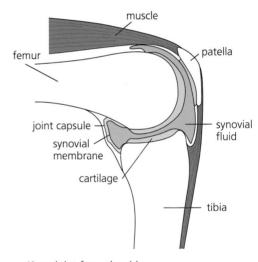

Knee joint from the side.

QUESTIONS

1 What is a joint?
2 Describe: **a** a fixed joint **b** a slightly moveable joint. Give two examples of each.
3 Which type of joint is the most common in your body? Give four examples.
4 **a** Draw and label a synovial joint. **b** Explain what job each part does.
5 Why do we need joints?

6 Name two ways a joint could be injured.
7 Name two actual injuries.
8 Which type of joint is the most useful for sport?
9 What parts of a synovial joint **a** make it strong and stable **b** help it move easily.

Discussion work
10 Choose one of your sports and discuss what impact injuries and what wear-and-tear injuries are common and why.

5.5   MOVEMENT

• • • • In this unit you will learn the types of movement possible at joints.

FLEXION AND EXTENSION

Extension means straightening a part of the body to its normal position.
Flexion means bending it. (**Flexion** is nearly always **F**orward.)

When you stand straight like this, your arms, legs, head, hands and feet are **extended** to their normal position.

Here the right arm is bent or flexed at the elbow joint. The left leg is **flexed** at the knee joint.

When you run you repeatedly flex and extend your hip, knee, ankle, elbow and shoulder joints.

Some more examples of flexion:

arm at
shoulder joint.

arm at elbow and
shoulder joint.

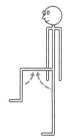

leg at hip and
knee joint.

back at
hip joints.

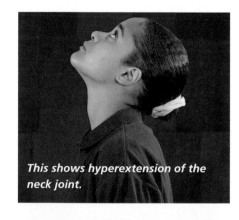

This shows hyperextension of the neck joint.

ABDUCTION AND ADDUCTION

Imagine a line drawn down the centre of your body. Abduction is a sideways movement of a limb, out from the centre line.

Adduction is a sideways movement, like this, towards and even across the centre line. (A**dd**uction is towards the mi**dd**le!)

This karate kick is an example of abduction. Can you think of another example from tennis? Or from gymnastics?

ROTATION AND CIRCUMDUCTION

These are circular movements.

Rotation is a turning movement around an imaginary line, like a wheel turning on its axis. Turning your head is an example.

This backwards walkover is another example. The girl's body is rotating like a wheel on an imaginary axis.

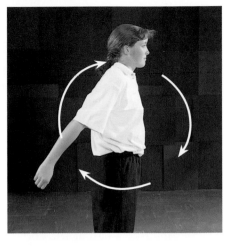

In circumduction, the end of a bone moves in a circle. Swinging your arm in a circle is an example. Bowlers do it!

JOINTS, FLEXIBILITY AND HEALTH

All of the movements shown require a degree of flexibility. Risk of injury can be lessened if we make our joints more flexible and strong. The first step in this is a good healthy diet, which will give us strong bones, ligaments, tendons and cartilage. Regular exercise will strengthen them all and regular flexibility work will allow a greater range of movement due to increased elasticity. Look at the karate picture opposite. This person can balance and apply a high kick due to good hip flexibility. In some joints you may wish to only have limited flexibility to reduce injury, e.g. shoulders in a rugby player.

A lack of exercise leads to a decrease in flexibility. This is a big problem for the elderly who find it difficult to do everyday tasks, e.g. turning a steering wheel and picking up shopping. Gentle exercise will help to remedy this.

QUESTIONS

1. Sit straight in your chair, elbows by your sides, hands flat on your knees, feet flat on the floor. **a** Which joints are flexed? **b** Name two joints that are extended.

2. Stand up and show an example of: **a** adduction **b** abduction

3. In swimming free style what movements occur at your hips?

4. In breast stroke what movements occur at your hips?

5. Stretch your arm straight out palm up. Turn your palm over. What movement occurred?

6. For the photo above: **a** name each numbered joint **b** name the movement that has occured at it to bring it to this position.

7. When doing the Fosbury flop in high jump you arch your back over the bar. What is the movement at your hips and vertebrae?

Discussion work

8. Choose one specific simple action from your sport. Discuss what movements are necessary at what joints to perform it.

5.6 SYNOVIAL JOINTS

• • • • In this unit you will learn the different types of synovial joints.

Most of your joints are freely moveable or synovial joints. They allow different kinds of movement, depending on the shape of the bones at the joint, and the ligaments that hold them together. The shoulder, hip and ankle are quite susceptible to injury due to the amount of movement possible at them. Sudden impact or over extension, etc. could cause dislocation or the tearing of ligaments and tendons.

These drawings show just the bones.

THE BALL-AND-SOCKET JOINT

This is the most moveable joint in the body. One bone has a bulge like a ball at the end. This fits into a socket in the other bone. It can turn in many directions.

Examples
◎ the hip joint. Cross over steps in badminton are caused by abduction and adduction, running comes from flexion and extension.
◎ the shoulder joint. Cricket bowling from circumduction, spin bowling in rounders from rotation.

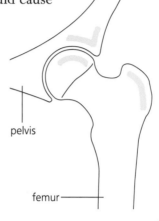

pelvis

femur

Hip joint.

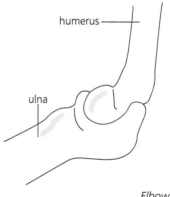

Types of movement:
ALL

THE HINGE JOINT

This works like a hinge on a door. The bone can swing backwards and forwards. The end of one bone is shaped like a cotton reel. It fits into a hollow in the other. The joint will open until it's straight, but no further.

Examples
◎ the elbow joint. Flexion and extension cause press-ups.
◎ the knee joint. Flexion and extension in horse riding cause rising trot.

humerus

ulna

Elbow joint.

Types of movement:
FLEXION and
EXTENSION

THE PIVOT JOINT

One bone has a bit that juts out, like a peg or a ridge. This fits into a ring or notch on the other bone. The joint allows only rotation.

Examples
◎ the joint between the atlas and axis, the top two bones of your vertebrae. Rotation results in looking from side to side.
◎ the joint between the radius and ulna, below the elbow. Rotation here results in changing from backhand to forehand in table tennis, squash and badminton.

atlas

vertebrae

axis

Joint in neck.

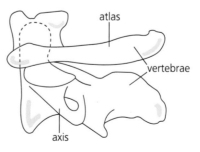

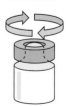

Types of movement:
ROTATION

THE GLIDING JOINT

Here the ends of the bones are flat enough to glide over each other. There is a little movement in all directions. Of all the synovial joints, this one gives least movement.

Examples

◎ the joints between carpals (hand) and tarsals (foot). Flexion and extension give final direction to a thrown object.

◎ the joints between most of the vertebrae. Rotation here helps to impart force in golf swings.

Types of movement:
FLEXION, EXTENSION, ABDUCTION AND ADDUCTION

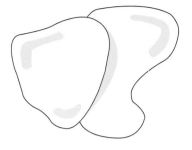

Joint between two carpals.

CARTILAGE, LIGAMENTS AND TENDONS

Cartilage protects bones and stops them knocking together. It forms a gristly cushion between the bones at slightly moveable joints. It forms a smooth slippery coat on the ends of bones at synovial joints.

Ligaments are the strong cords and straps that lash bones together and hold a joint in place. They are just a bit elastic – enough to let the bones move. (If bones moved too much they would tear your flesh.)

Tendons are the cords and straps that connect muscle to bone. The best known joins our calf muscle to our heel and is called the Achilles tendon.

JOINTS AND MOVEMENT: A SUMMARY

This is a summary of the different kinds of movement that different joints allow.

> **DID YOU KNOW?**
> In ancient Greek legends Achilles was a man who could not be harmed by any weapon because he had been dipped in dragon's blood as a baby. Unfortunately, he was held by the heel and no blood reached this spot. He was eventually killed by a poisoned arrow that hit him just above his heel. Even today we call this our 'Achilles tendon'.

Type of joint	Movement allowed
ball-and-socket	flexion and extension
	abduction and adduction
	rotation and circumduction
hinge	flexion and extension
pivot	only rotation
gliding	a little gliding in all directions (no bending or circular movements)

QUESTIONS

1 Look at the shape of the ball-and-socket joint. Why do you think it is difficult to dislocate it?

2 What are the major joints (location and type) that are moving when you are running?

3 In what joint would a cricket bowler want to be very flexible?

4 Why would players of American football and rugby not want to be flexible in this particular joint?

5 In what joints would a batter in any sport want to be flexible?

6 Where in our body do we find **a** cartilage **b** ligaments **c** tendons? (In a joint is not enough.)

7 Name one tendon.

8 Why do you think that it is difficult to improve flexibility at a hinge joint?

Discussion work

9 In one of your sports discuss the actions that are commonplace that use each of the joints in this unit.

5.7   BONE AND JOINT INJURIES (1)

• • • • In these two units you will learn the potential joint and bone injuries and their basic treatment.

Sports injuries can be very painful. They can ruin an athlete's career. Some can take years to heal properly. So avoid them if you can!

Whilst it is very useful to have a first aid qualification, it is sufficient to know basic treatment to keep a casualty comfortable and to know when you need to send for further help.

TWO KINDS OF SPORTS INJURIES

All sports injuries fall into two groups:

◎ injuries caused by a sudden stress on the body, such as a violent collision. Such injuries are common in contact sports like rugby.
◎ injuries which develop through overuse. Tennis players may suffer from tennis elbow and runners from an inflamed Achilles tendon. Overuse injuries can be brought on by heavy training programmes, insufficient rest between events, poor technique, or badly designed footwear or equipment.

TREATMENT

1 **Danger**: ensure that you will not put yourself into danger whilst treating the casualty – stop the game, use a rope or piece of clothing to pull a swimmer into you, and so on. Check the casualty themselves is in no further danger by removing them to the sideline if it is safe to do so, or again making sure that the activity has stopped.
2 **Response**: ask the casualty what they are feeling and what happened. If they cannot respond, call for help and get an ambulance.
3 For minor injuries you can treat the casualty using **RICE**.

RICE

When bones, joints, ligaments, muscles or tendons get damaged, the blood vessels around them get damaged too. Blood leaks into the surrounding tissue. This causes swelling, pain and bruising, and slows down healing. So the aim of RICE is to stop the blood leaking.

◎ **R**est. Movement keeps the blood leaking. Keep the part still.
◎ **I**ce. Place an icepack around the injured part for 30 minutes or so. Cold makes blood vessels constrict and this reduces bleeding.
◎ **C**ompression. Bandage the injured part firmly but not tightly, using a crepe bandage. This reduces bleeding.
◎ **E**levate the injured limb. This reduces blood flow to the limb because the blood has to flow against gravity.

*A football injury. Injury like this, due to a collision or other sudden stress, is often described as **acute**. Injury due to overuse is described as **chronic**.*

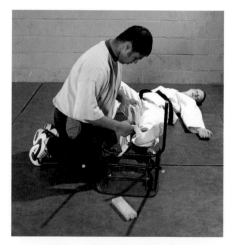

RICE treatment under way. To elevate the injured limb use whatever support is available.

SPRAIN

A **sprain** occurs when a ligament at a joint gets stretched and torn. Twisting your foot when running can give you a sprained ankle. Landing awkwardly in any jumping sport is also a common way to do this. Some sprains are minor, but in a severe sprain the ligament is badly torn and the injury looks like a fracture. If in doubt, treat it as a fracture.

Signs and symptoms
◎ There is pain and tenderness around the joint, and movement makes it worse.
◎ Swelling appears around the joint, followed later by bruising.

What you can do
◎ If in doubt, follow the instructions for a fracture.
◎ For minor sprains follow the **RICE** routine from the previous page.

With minor sprains you may be tempted to play on. It depends upon the pain and if you can still move properly as to whether this is sensible.

REHABILITATION

This may be from 1 week to 3 months and the treatment can involve taking anti-inflammatory medication to reduce swelling and having massage and ultrasound from a physiotherapist.

TORN CARTILAGE

Remember your joints have pieces, or pads, of cartilage to absorb shock. These may tear when the joint is twisted violently. This is called torn cartilage.

Signs and symptoms
◎ There is pain on one side of the joint.
◎ The joint may 'lock' and not straighten fully for a time.
◎ It may swell later that day or next morning.

What you can do
◎ Use an icepack to reduce the swelling.
◎ Get the athlete to the doctor.

Torn cartilage can only be repaired by surgery, but it very often cannot make the joint as good as it was before the injury.

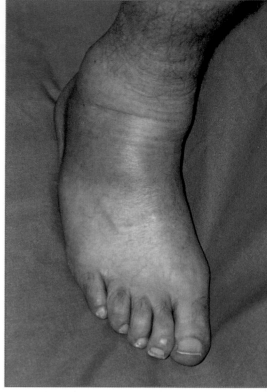

Sprained ankles can be very painful.

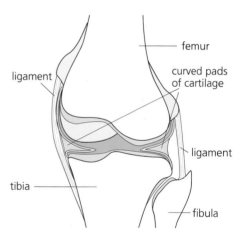

The cartilage pads in the knee.

(labels: femur, curved pads of cartilage, ligament, ligament, tibia, fibula)

QUESTIONS

1 List four ways a sudden stress can cause injury in sport.
2 What does RICE stand for?
3 What is the purpose of the **I** from RICE?
4 What is the purpose of the **C** from RICE?
5 What is the purpose of the **E** from RICE?

6 What problems may be brought on by using fashion trainers instead of proper sports ones?

Discussion work

7 Discuss why you think massage and ultrasound can help to heal injuries. (N.b. ultrasound creates heat deep inside your muscles and joints. Blood likes to travel to warm muscles.)

5.8 BONE AND JOINT INJURIES (2)

• • • • In this unit you will learn more about the potential joint and bone injuries and their basic treatment.

TENNIS AND GOLFER'S ELBOW

These are muscle injuries caused by overuse of muscles in the lower arm. In tennis elbow the area around the outer bony bump on the elbow is inflamed, tender and painful. This injury can occur in fishing as well as racket sports. In golfer's elbow the area around the inner bony bump is affected.

What you can do
◎ If the injury is very painful, an icepack will help.
◎ The elbow must be rested until it recovers, which could take weeks.
◎ The usual treatment is physiotherapy and injection of a steroid into the muscle.

DISLOCATION

This is where a bone is pulled out of its normal position at a joint. It is usually caused by violent twisting. It usually happens at the shoulder, elbow, finger, thumb and ankle joints. Dislocation and fracture often go together. If in doubt, treat as a fracture.

Signs and symptoms
◎ There is severe pain at or near the joint.
◎ The joint appears deformed and the casualty can't move it.
◎ There is swelling, and bruising appears later.

What you can do
◎ Dial 999 for an ambulance.
◎ Support the injured part using clothing, towels or cushions.
◎ Support injured elbow or finger joints with slings or bandages.

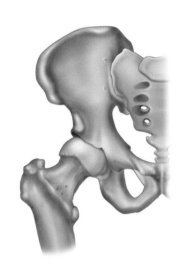

Normal hip joint.

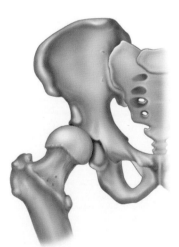

Dislocated hip joint.

FRACTURES

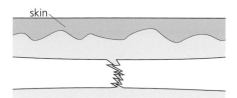

This is a simple or closed fracture. The bone is cracked but the skin is not damaged.

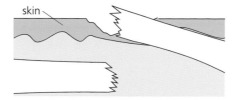

This is an open or compound fracture. The skin is damaged and the bone may stick out.

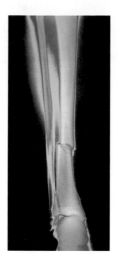

An X-ray showing a closed fracture of the tibia or shinbone. (Colour has been added to show up the fracture more clearly.)

A *fracture* is a break or crack in a bone. Since bones contain nerves and blood vessels, a fracture brings pain and bleeding. Bleeding leads to *swelling* and *bruising* when the blood leaks into the surrounding tissue.

Signs and symptoms
◎ The casualty may have heard or felt a snap.
◎ There is pain and tenderness around the injury. Moving makes it worse.
◎ The casualty will not be able to move the part normally.
◎ The bleeding leads to swelling. Bruising develops later.
◎ The limb may look deformed. For example a foot may be twisted backwards. To check, compare the two limbs.
◎ There may be a grating noise when the parts of the cracked bone rub against each other. But don't try to test for this!

What you can do
◎ Dial 999 for an ambulance.
◎ Do *not* move the casualty and do not try to straighten the fractured limb, since this will make the damage worse.
◎ Support the limb above and below the fracture using towels, cushions or folded clothing.
◎ If the fracture is in an arm bone, a sling made of a towel, bandage or T-shirt can be used for support. But be very careful!

OTHER TYPES OF FRACTURE

Stress fractures
High impact sports where a bone is repeatedly used on a hard surface, e.g. running, can lead to stress fractures – cracks in the bone.

Greenstick fractures
Usually associated with young bone which is still pliable, this type of fracture is where the bone is not broken completely from one side to the other.

Spiral fractures
Created when the bone is being twisted as it breaks.

The more common type of fracture in sport is the contact injury, as shown below.

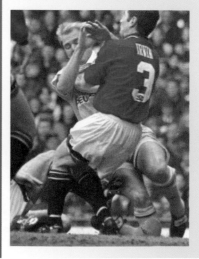

Contact can lead to many injuries as shown above with Dave Busst's broken leg.

QUESTIONS

1 You are a sports physiotherapist. What injuries do you suspect might have occurred from the following scenarios?

  a When jumping for a jump ball in basketball a player lands awkwardly and says their ankle hurts.

  b After a tackle in rugby a player complains of a really bad shoulder.

  c Whilst moving for a shot in tennis the ball is unexpectedly put to the other side of the court. The player twists to reach it but gets a terrible pain their knee.

2 For each of the suspected injuries above what signs and symptoms would you expect to see?

3 What treatment for each of the above injuries would you recommend?

Discussion work

4 Discuss any recent sports injuries you have heard of in the media. Who did they happen to, what was their treatment and what was the timescale for their recovery?

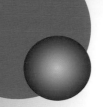
QUESTIONS ON CHAPTER 5

1

a   Write the numbers 1 to 20 in a list, to match the numbers on the skeleton above.

b   Beside each number write the correct scientific name for the bone.

2 Bones are long, short, irregular or flat. To which group do these bones belong?

a   the bones of the cranium

b   the humerus

c   the carpals of the hand

d   the metatarsals

e   the bones of the pelvis

f   the vertebrae.

3 What bones are most likely to get damaged in football? Will it be wear and tear or impact?

4 What safety item is worn to reduce this risk?

5 The most common impact injuries in netball and basketball are in the fingers and ankles. Why is this?

6 What damage could be done by dislocating a finger?

7 In sports involving running or jumping on a hard surface, ankle and knee joints can get worn out. Explain how this occurs.

8 How do the ribs help protect us?

9 How can bones help us move?

10 The bones of a fit person produce more blood cells than those of unfit people. Why is this important to a sports person?

11 What three nutrients are essential for strong bones?

12 Why shouldn't children and teenagers lift heavy weights in regular strength training?

13 Which of your three types of joints are most useful in sport?

14 As young bones grow, bone replaces cartilage. What is this process called?

A   ossification

B   osteoarthritis

C   osteopathy

D   osteoporosis

15 Copy this table. Then complete it by filling in the everyday names of the bones.

Bone	Everyday name
cranium	skull
scapula	
sternum	
clavicle	
femur	
phalanges (foot)	
metatarsals	
tarsals	
tibia	
patella	
phalanges (hand)	
metacarpals	

16 The drawing below shows joints of the body:

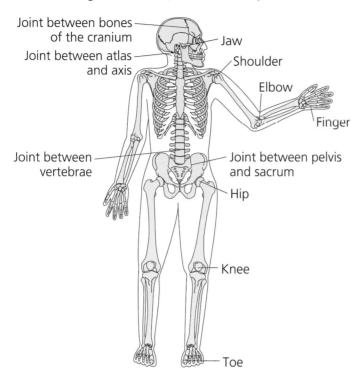

Joint between bones of the cranium
Joint between atlas and axis
Joint between vertebrae
Jaw
Shoulder
Elbow
Finger
Joint between pelvis and sacrum
Hip
Knee
Toe

a Make a table with five columns. Write these five headings on the columns:

| Fixed | Slightly moveable | Ball-and-socket |
| Hinge | Pivot | |

b Now write each joint from the drawing in the correct column in the table.

17 Answer these questions about bones.
  a Name a substance that is needed to form strong and healthy bones.
  b Give two examples of foods which will provide this substance.
  c What job does the cartilage on the ends of the bones do?
  d Bones have spongy parts. How does this help you in playing sports?
  e In which part of the bone are red blood cells made?
  f Are red cells made in all bones?
  g Around what age does the skeleton stop growing?

18 a Draw and label an adult long bone.
  b Now write what each part of the bone does.

USE OF INFORMATION TECHNOLOGY

19 Typing the following phrases into a search engine on the internet will give you many sites to explore.
  a skeleton, bones, -fossil, -prehistoric (note: the - sign means you will get rid of sites containing the words fossil and prehistoric)
  b bone, marrow, ossification, calcium, -fossil, -prehistoric
  c bone, joint, injury

APPLIED QUESTIONS

A20 You have been training for a year for health reasons. You have worked mainly on stamina by jogging three evenings a week and doing a weekly aerobics session.
  a How would the composition of your bones be different from a year ago?
  b Sport, as you know, has very specific effects. What main bones will be affected by your training?
  c Your 12-year-old daughter wants to run with you in the evenings. You let her do the part of your run that goes over the grass but will not let her do the full distance or road running. Why did you make that decision?
  d An elderly friend of yours asks you whether she should do some exercise. What advice would you give her and why?
  e You have badly grazed and bruised you left knee but carry on with your running schedule. Strangely, a week later your right knee and ankle feel a bit sore. Can you account for this?

6.1   DIFFERENT KINDS OF MUSCLE

● ● ● ● ● In this unit you will learn about the different types of muscle in the body.

You could not live without muscles. You couldn't breathe or digest food or even blink. They are involved in every movement of your body, inside and out.

All muscles work by shortening or *contracting*. When muscles between your mouth and jaw bones contract, you smile!

There are three different kinds of muscle in your body.

VOLUNTARY MUSCLE

This is attached to bones. It works when you want it to. Voluntary means by your own free will.

Suppose you decide to run or throw a ball. A signal races from your brain, along your nervous system, to the voluntary muscles needed for this job. The muscles contract, pulling on bones. This gives movement.

Voluntary muscle is also called:
◎ **skeletal muscle** because it is attached to bones
◎ **striped muscle** because when you look at it under a miscroscope you can see stripes across it.

INVOLUNTARY MUSCLE

This is found in the walls of your internal organs: stomach, gut, bladder and blood vessels. It is called involuntary because it works on its own. You don't need to think about it.

When you digest food, the involuntary muscle in the walls of your gut contracts in waves, pushing the food along. In the same way, contractions in the walls of blood vessels help to keep blood flowing.

Involuntary muscle is also called **smooth muscle** because it looks smooth under a microscope, with no stripes.

CARDIAC MUSCLE

This is special involuntary muscle that forms the walls of your heart. It works non-stop without tiring. Like voluntary muscle, it is striped. When it contracts, it pumps blood out of your heart and round your body. Each contraction is a heartbeat.

MORE ABOUT VOLUNTARY MUSCLE

Voluntary muscles form the red meat round your bones. They give shape to your body. Over 40% of your weight is voluntary muscle. So if you weigh 50 kilograms, over 20 kilograms of that is due to voluntary muscle.

With training we can adapt our muscles to help make us better at exercise. There is more on this later in the chapter.

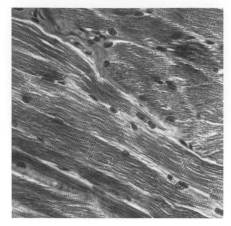

Voluntary muscle fibres, stained with dye to show up the stripes and magnified by 200. The fibres at the top left are in cross-section.

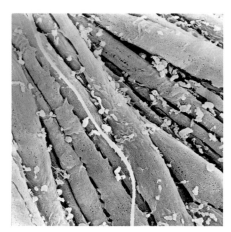

Smooth muscle fibres, magnified by 900. The wavy yellow line is a nerve.

MUSCLE FIBRES

Muscles are made up of cells called muscle fibres. Muscles contract (shorten) because the fibres do. But they don't all contract together. The number contracting at any one time depends on how much force is needed, e.g. more fibres in your biceps contract when you lift this book than when you lift a pencil.

There are two different kinds of muscle fibres, **slow twitch** and **fast twitch**.

FAST AND SLOW TWITCH FIBRES

Which sports are you best at? It partly depends on the mixture of slow and fast twitch fibres in your muscles.

Slow twitch fibres contract slowly, and without much force. But they do not tire easily. So they are suited to activities that need endurance, e.g. jogging, long-distance running, and standing for long periods.

Fast twitch fibres contract much faster than slow twitch fibres, and with much more force. But they tire quickly. So they are suited to activities that need bursts of strength and power, e.g. sprinting and weightlifting.

Every muscle contains a mixture of these fibres. But:

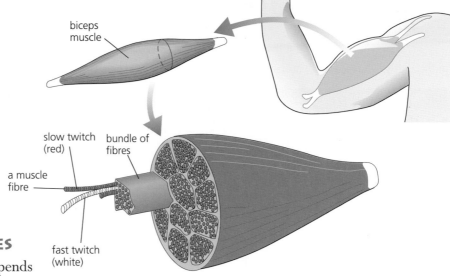

biceps muscle

slow twitch (red) bundle of fibres

a muscle fibre

fast twitch (white)

> **Blame your parents!**
> You are born with a mix of slow and fast twitch fibres. Even with training you cannot change one to the other.

The mixture is different in different muscles. For example your gastrocnemius contains a lot of fast twitch fibres. Standing on your toes gets tiring!

The mixture is different for different people. Some distance runners have 80% slow twitch fibres while some weight lifters have 80% fast twitch fibres.

Why the difference? It's all your parents' fault! You inherited the mixture from them and it's too late to change it now...

QUESTIONS

1 **a** Name the three kinds of muscle at work in your body as you answer this question. **b** Give examples of each of them.

2 What are the other names for voluntary muscle?

3 What is the proper name for muscle cells?

4 Name a muscle that usually has mainly fast twitch fibres.

Discussion work

5 Choose two very different types of sporting activity and discuss what would be the ideal percentage of slow and fast muscle fibres for you to have in order to do it well.

6.2 THE MUSCULAR SYSTEM

• • • • In this unit you will learn about names and functions of the main muscles.

Muscle		Main action(s)
1	deltoid	Raises your arm sideways at the shoulder.
2	biceps	Bends your arm at the elbow.
3	abdominals (4 muscles)	Pull in your abdomen. Flex your trunk so you can bend forward.
4	quadriceps (4 muscles)	Straighten your leg at the knee and keep it straight when you stand.
5	pectorals	Raises your arm at the shoulder. Draws it across your chest.
6	latissimus dorsi	Pulls your arm down at the shoulder. Draws it behind your back.
7	trapezius	Holds and rotates your shoulders. Moves your head back and sideways.
8	triceps	Straightens your arm at the elbow joint.
9	gluteals (3 muscles)	Pull your leg back at the hip. Raise it sideways at the hip. Gluteus maximus is the biggest of these muscles.
10	hamstrings (3 muscles)	Bend your leg at the knee.
11	gastrocnemius	Straightens the ankle joint so you can stand on your tiptoes.

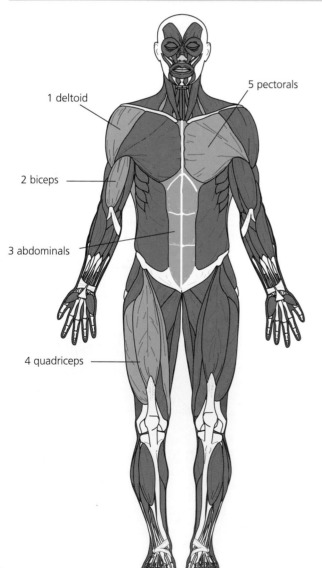

1 deltoid

5 pectorals

2 biceps

3 abdominals

4 quadriceps

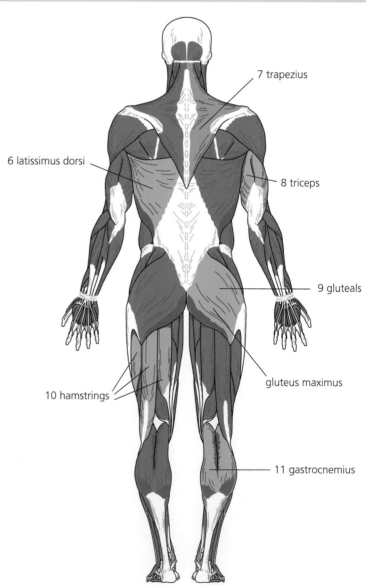

7 trapezius

6 latissimus dorsi

8 triceps

9 gluteals

gluteus maximus

10 hamstrings

11 gastrocnemius

Trapezius –
has pulled the head back to look at the shuttlecock.
Other examples: bringing head back as you arch over bar in Fosbury flop in high jump.

Deltoid –
has raised (or abducted) the arm at the shoulder.
Other examples: holding arms out to balance on the beam in gymnastics.

Biceps –
has bent (or flexed) the elbow.
Other examples: bending elbow for rowing.

Triceps –
is just going to start straightening the elbow (extension) to hit the shuttlecock.
Other examples: straighten elbow when rowing.

Latissimus dorsi (lower back) –
will pull arms down (adduct) after the shot has been played.
Other examples: pulling the arm down after throwing a javelin.

Gluteals –
have pulled this leg back at the hip slightly (extended it).
Other examples: pulling the leg back prior to kicking a ball in football AND pulling the leg out sideways at the hip (abduction), e.g. sidestepping.

Abdominals –
will soon have to work to straighten the spine again.
Other examples: pulling your upper body down as you go over a hurdle.

Hamstrings –
have bent (or flexed) the knee slightly.
Other examples: any jumping activity which requires you to bend your knees prior to take-off.

Quadriceps –
are just about to be used to straighten (or extend) the legs at the knee.
Other examples: straightening knees as you jump.

Gastrocnemius –
is being used to go up on tiptoes to push back to the ready position after striking the shuttlecock.
Other examples: any running or jumping activity, or pointing toes in gymnastics.

QUESTIONS

1 Where are these muscles and what job do they do?
   a pectorals **b** biceps **c** triceps **d** deltoids **e** hamstrings **f** quadriceps.
2 Imagine performing a jump shot in basketball. What muscles are used to straighten your legs as you jump?
3 Which muscle contracts when you look upwards?

4 When running what muscles are used to: **a** bend/flex your knee? **b** pull your hip back after the step? **c** straighten, or extend, your knee?

Discussion work

5 Choose a stance from your sport (like with the badminton player above) and discuss what muscles have moved your limbs into these positions.

6.3 MUSCLES AND MOVEMENT

In this unit you will learn about how muscles are attached and how they work.

A voluntary muscle usually works across a joint. It is attached to both the bones by strong cords called **tendons**.

When the muscle contracts, usually just one bone moves.

For example when the biceps in the arm contracts, the radius moves but the scapula does not.

When a muscle contracts, usually just one bone moves. The other is stationary. The *origin* is where the muscle joins the stationary bone (1 in the diagram above). The *insertion* is where it joins the moving bone (2). When a muscle contracts, **the insertion moves towards the origin**.

Muscles usually work in pairs or groups, e.g. the biceps flexes the elbow and the triceps extends it.

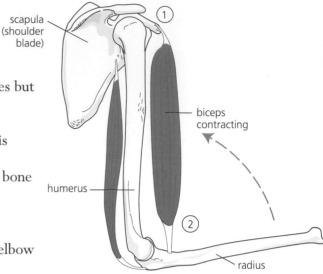

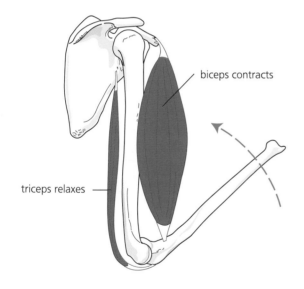

To flex the elbow the biceps contracts (shortens) and the triceps relaxes (lengthens).

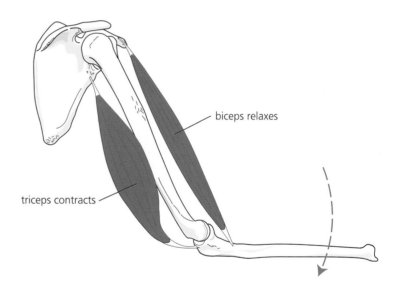

To extend the elbow, the biceps relaxes and the triceps contracts.

This is called antagonistic muscle action. The working muscle is called the prime mover or agonist. (It's in agony!) The relaxing muscle is the antagonist. The other main pair of muscles that work together are the quadriceps and hamstrings. Imagine the picture above is a bent knee. Which muscle would be the agonist as the knee is bent (flexed) and then extended?

The prime mover is helped by other muscles called **synergists**. These contract at the same time as the prime mover. They hold the body in position so that the prime mover can work smoothly.

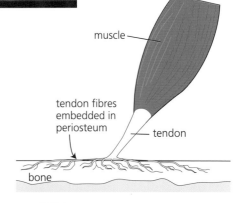

A network of muscles act as synergists to help hold her in position for this move.

Goal! To straighten the knee in the last stage of the kick, the quadriceps acted as agonist and the hamstrings as antagonist.

As mentioned previously, tendons are the cords and straps that connect muscles to bones. At the bone, the fibres of the tendon are embedded in the periosteum of the bone. This anchors the tendon strongly and spreads the force of the contraction, so the tendon won't tear away easily.

muscle

tendon fibres embedded in periosteum

tendon

bone

MUSCLE TONE

Even when a muscle is relaxed, a small number of its fibres are contracted – enough to keep the muscle taut but not enough to cause movement. This state of partial contraction is called **muscle tone**. Without muscle tone you could not stand up straight!

Gravity tries to pull your head forward, as shown here. But partial contraction or muscle tone in the trapezius will keep it upright.

Muscle tone in the quadriceps balances the muscle tone in the hamstrings to keep your legs straight at the knee.

If the muscle tone in your abdominals is poor, your spine curves in too much. This leads to poor posture.

To maintain muscle tone without getting tired, groups of muscle fibres take it in turn to contract. They work in relays. Poor muscle tone leads to poor posture. But exercise improves muscle tone. It makes the muscle fibres thicker so they contract more strongly.

QUESTIONS

1 To jump we bend our legs and then straighten them.
   a What main pair of muscles help move the knee?
   b What is this working in pairs called?

2 Give an example from one of your chosen sports of antagonistic muscle action.

3 What muscle is the prime mover when **a** doing a sit-up?
   b doing the upwards phase of a press-up?

4 **a** Draw a diagram to show how the biceps works.
   b Why doesn't the scapula move?

5 Explain how having poor muscle tone can cause bad posture.

Discussion work

6 Choose two movements from your sport, one using your legs and one your arms. Discuss how antagonistic muscle action helps you perform these movements.

6.4 MUSCLES AND EXERCISE

● ● ● ● In this unit you will learn the effects of exercise on muscles.

To recap so far, muscles cross joints and when they contract they shorten. This pulls the bones together. One bone tends to stay still and the other gets pulled towards it. The points of attachment are the *origin* and *insertion*, the insertion gets pulled towards the origin. Muscles usually work in pairs. You are expected to know the easy ones; biceps/triceps and hamstrings/quadriceps. This working in pairs is called **antagonistic** muscle action and the **agonist** is the muscle that shortens. Muscles are generally made to work quickly and powerfully (fast twitch) or for long periods of time (slow twitch).

HOW MUSCLE SPEED AFFECTS PERFORMANCE

The more fast twitch fibres you have, the more suited you are to sports that need bursts of strength and power. When you play just for fun, the fibre mix does not matter. But at higher levels it can make the difference between winning and losing.

Suppose two sprinters X and Y are competing. They are the same age and weight and at the same level of fitness. But X has 75% fast twitch fibre in her leg muscles and Y has only 55%. So X should be able to start faster, accelerate faster and sprint faster than Y. She has a better chance of winning.

THE IMMEDIATE EFFECTS OF EXERCISE

Fatigue is mental or physical exhaustion. When fast twitch fibres work maximally for too long they fatigue, e.g. the 400-metre sprint; any game activity where you sprint yourself to a standstill; the end of a floor routine in gym; canoe sprinting; downhill racing in skiing, etc.

The fatigue is caused by the build up of a poisonous substance – lactic acid. It causes pain and prevents any more energy from being supplied to the muscles.

When slow twitch fibres work for several hours they can also fatigue. If the exercise was gentle, the fatigue tends to be due to the body running out of glucose (stored as glycogen). The muscles literally run out of energy.

MUSCLES AND TRAINING

Training and exercise have long-term effects on our muscles but if we stop exercising they return to their original state (reversibility).

Cardiac muscle. This grows bigger and stronger (this is called hypertrophy). This means more blood is pumped around the body which means more oxygen can reach the voluntary muscles.

Voluntary muscles. These also grow bigger and stronger. You would need to know whether your sport needs mainly fast twitch or slow twitch fibres, so you can train this area.

Top sprinters have a lot of fast twitch muscle fibres.

Running out of energy in long distance events, such as the marathon, can cause your muscles to completely give way.

Fast twitch fibres. With training these can contract more strongly. This would help improve your performance in maximum-effort activities, e.g. throwing events in athletics, jumping, sprinting, smashes in tennis and badminton, etc. You can also delay the build up of lactic acid for a few seconds. This doesn't sound much but if you can run the 100 metres in 14 seconds, you can cover about 20 metres in 3 seconds. Just think how useful this would be in many sports.

Slow twitch fibres. With the correct training and diet your body adapts to store more glycogen and you get used to using fat as an energy source. Most of us have plenty of that! Lots of energy can be obtained by the breakdown of fat but without training it takes a very long time before it begins to be used.

TRAINING, EVERYDAY LIFE AND LONG-TERM BENEFITS

Gentle exercise combining strength work and stamina will help our hearts and muscles become stronger and fitter and help us with our general fitness for everyday tasks. After illness this must be done very gradually.

Muscle training is very important for older people. As mentioned in chapter 1, muscle strength is at its peak at about 25 years old, plateaus (keeps level) until 40 and then drops quite a lot. This loss of strength can impede everyday living – carrying groceries, etc. – so it is vital to keep training. Regular load-bearing exercise can also help prevent, or slow down, the weakening of bones (mentioned in chapter 5). Obviously huge weights are not necessary and it is better to concentrate on gentle endurance work as described in the next few pages.

Gentle endurance work is very important for older people.

All muscle changes are reversible:
IF YOU DO NOT USE IT YOU LOSE IT!

MUSCLE TRAINING AND FLEXIBILITY

Poor flexibility can cause poor performance, either due to injury or poor/inefficient technique. It can hinder both speed and endurance as the muscle has to work harder to overcome resistance. If you can combine strength work with flexibility then the muscle can contract more strongly along a full range of movement to provide maximum strength and power. Strength training without flexibility can cause individuals to become 'muscle-bound' and restricted in movement.

Flexibility training is very important for the elderly, as tendons and ligaments become less elastic. This could cause injury and prevent many movements, e.g. getting into a car or bath. For those very weak or suffering from arthritis this can be done in a pool where the warmth increases joint flexibility and body weight is supported.

QUESTIONS

1 Which of these training methods suit which fibres: **a** long distance cycling **b** sprint work **c** circuit training with bursts of 20-seconds' activity **d** walking fast for thirty minutes?

2 Explain two important reasons why gentle training is important to older people.

3 If following a weights programme, why is it vital to work on flexibility?

4 Whilst racing a friend flat-out you have to stop due to the pain in your leg muscles. What is this caused by?

Discussion work

5 Discuss using two sports of your choice why the delaying of the build-up of lactic acid, for even a few seconds, could be extremely useful.

6.5 MUSCLES AND FLEXIBILITY TRAINING

● ● ● ● ● In this unit you will learn the ways in which a muscle can contract and be trained.

Here are two different ways to train muscles, based on different kinds of muscle contraction. Both involve pulling or pushing or lifting a load.

ISOTONIC TRAINING

To bend your arm at the elbow, your biceps muscle shortens. This is called an **isotonic contraction**. All your body movements depend on isotonic contractions, when muscles shorten and pull on bones. Isotonic contractions can also be called **dynamic contractions**.

In **isotonic training** you use isotonic contractions to improve your muscle strength and endurance. Press-ups, sit-ups, chins and weightlifting are isotonic exercises. Can you think of others?

Advantages of isotonic training

◎ It strengthens a muscle through the full range of movement.
◎ You can choose isotonic exercises to suit your sport.

Disadvantages

◎ It can make muscles sore. This is caused by stress on muscles while they lengthen. For example, there is stress on your arm muscles when you lower your body during chins.
◎ You gain most muscle strength at the weakest point of the action. You don't gain it evenly throughout.

ISOMETRIC TRAINING

When you push against a closed door, your arm muscles contract but stay the same length. This is called an **isometric contraction**.

Isometric contractions produce **static strength**. This is the strength you need to push or pull a very heavy object or hold up a heavy load. You need it in sumo wrestling, a rugby scrum, gymnastics and weightlifting. **Isometric training** uses isometric contractions to strengthen your muscles. It can help for these sports.

Advantages of isometric training

◎ It is quick to do and does not hurt.
◎ It does not need expensive equipment.
◎ You can do it anywhere.

Disadvantages

◎ A muscle gains strength only at the angle you use in the exercise. This might not help much in your sport.
◎ During isometric exercise, the blood flow to the muscle stops, blood pressure rises, and less blood flows back to the heart. This could be dangerous if you have heart problems.

Isometric training is best if you combine it with isotonic training.

An isotonic exercise, since muscles are contracting. But which muscles? And what's the advantage of the machine over free weights?

A static exercise, as muscles are contracting but no movement is occuring.

IMPROVING FLEXIBILITY

Earlier in this chapter we looked at the importance of improving strength **and** flexibility. One developed without the other is not beneficial to your body and indeed could lead to injuries, e.g. strains.

STRAINED OR PULLED MUSCLES

A strain or pull is a tear in a muscle or its tendon, caused by violent over-stretching. It often happens with hamstrings and calf muscles, especially if you don't warm up properly. The Achilles tendon of the calf muscle (gastrocnemius) can tear completely. That is very painful.

You feel a sharp pain at the site of the injury. This is followed by swelling and stiffness.

STRETCHING

You improve **flexibility** through **static stretching**.

*In **static stretching**, a muscle is held in a stretched position for a number of seconds. This can be done actively or passively.*

*In **active stretching**, you do the work. Don't jerk or bounce. Only stretch as far as is comfortable.*

*In **passive stretching** your partner does the work, holding you in a stretch for several seconds. Be careful. Too much force can injure you.*

The joint capsule controls around half the movement at a joint. The rest depends mainly on muscles and tendons. When you stretch, your muscles and tendons get stretched. This makes them more flexible so the joint can move more freely. A flexible joint is at less risk of strain. So stretching is part of the warm up for every training session. Flexibility is also linked to **strength**. Muscles that are stretched well can contract more strongly.

QUESTIONS

1 What is an **isotonic** contraction?

2 What is an **isometric** contraction?

3 What kind of contraction do you use when you:

    a run? **b** pull on the rope in a tug-of-war?

4 Give two advantages of isotonic training.

5 Name two isotonic exercises **not** mentioned here.

6 Give two advantages of isometric training.

7 What is the difference between active and passive stretching?

Discussion work

8 Discuss using rock climbing as an example, the use of isotonic and isometric contractions.

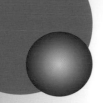
QUESTIONS ON CHAPTER 6

1 What three different types of muscle are there?

2 Which two of these are the most important with regards to sport.

3 Raj has been in hospital with a badly broken leg and has done no exercise for four months. Her doctor recommends a programme of slow walking with a gradual increase in speed and distance. What two muscular benefits will she gain?

4 Voluntary muscles can be mainly fast or slow twitch fibres. If you did a survey of the following world-class athletes, what would you expect to find in terms of these?

  a Shot-putter
  b Marathon runner
  c Rounders player
  d High-jumper
  e Channel swimmer
  f Rugby player

5 Matt wants to improve his muscles for javelin throwing by training. He decides to run three miles a day. Would this help him improve his distance? Explain.

6 What muscles cause the movement shown at joints 1, 2 and 4 and what movement occurs at them all?

7 Some sports need a mixture of slow and fast twitch muscle fibres. Why do you think a boxer would train his upper body for power (fast twitch) and his lower body for stamina (slow twitch).

8 While doing a biceps curl the prime mover is the biceps. Other muscles hold the body in position. What are they called?

9 Are the muscles below voluntary, involuntary or cardiac?
  a The heart muscle
  b The muscle around your bladder
  c The biceps
  d The trapezius
  e The muscle in your artery wall.

10 Give another name for voluntary and involuntary muscles.

11 Unless you are unconscious, your muscles are always partly contracted.
  a What is this condition called?
  b Explain how it helps you to hold your head up.
  c Explain how it helps you to look better.
  d Why do the muscles not get tired?

12 Each muscle in your body is a mixture of two types of muscle fibres, slow twitch and fast twitch.
  a Which gives the strongest contractions?
  b Which tires most easily?
  c Which can keep going for longer?
  d 'The more you exercise the more fast twitch fibres you have.' Is this statement true? Explain your answer.

13 Which type of muscle fibre do you depend on for:
  a jogging?
  b doing a back somersault?
  c lifting a really heavy weight?
  d carrying your books home from school?
  e working behind the counter in a shop?
  f a 100m swimming race?
  g playing golf?
  h pulling in a tug-of-war?
  i playing a tennis match?

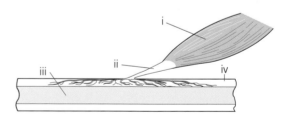

14 The above diagram shows where a muscle joins to a bone.
  a Name the numbered parts.
  b Part ii is deeply embedded in part iv. Why?

15 A softball player decides to get really fit for their sport and starts weight training in the off-season (winter). They decide to build up their strength and then nearer the start of the season make it more specific.

  a What sort of weights programme would you set for the winter and why?

  b What area of strength would the player concentrate on nearer the start of the season and why?

  c How would you change their programme at this point?

  d If the player was under 16, what kinds of weights would you recommend and why?

  e Should this person concentrate on isotonic or isometric work? Explain.

  f By the start of the season this player has really improved their fitness, particularly the muscles of the trunk and shoulders. Unfortunately, because they were pushed for time when training in the evenings, they neglected any flexibility work. What problems can you foresee?

16 For actions a–d below, say which muscles you think are the agonists and which are the antagonists.

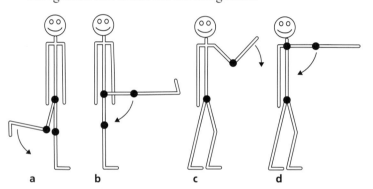

  a   b   c   d

(The drawings on page 90 will help you.)

17 Give the anatomical name for the muscles listed below:

calf	stomach
chest	shoulder
front of thigh	bottom
back of thigh	lower back

18 Christine is the national under-15 javelin champion. After several months of flexibility training her performance improves. Why could this be?

USE OF INFORMATION TECHNOLOGY

19 Using a digital camera (or normal camera and scanner) take some pictures of your sport. Using the major muscles, label it as done for the badminton player on page 89. Make the best examples into posters for your PE classroom.

20 Collect data for your group for the sit-up and the vertical jump tests. Put the results into a spreadsheet and produce a scatter graph. Is there a relationship between the results of these tests? Explain your answer.

21 Repeat the data collection for the other tests and compare results to find any relationships. Use that information to say whether the following relationships are true for your group.

  a A person who is good at the grip test is also good at the vertical jump test.

  b People who are good in one test tend to be good in all the tests.

APPLIED QUESTIONS

Louise and her friend Paul are both very good sports people. Paul really likes rock climbing and decides he could do with being fitter to help him in the more difficult moves. Louise is a hockey player. It is currently June and she wants to start the season already being fit. They are both 18.

A22 Explain what you think the best physique for these sports would be.

A23 For what reasons should Louise and Paul not do the same training schedule?

A24 Make an analysis of each of Louise and Paul's training needs (refer to 6.1 and 2.3) with regard to correct muscle groups, specific areas of fitness, the correct energy systems and whether pressure training is required.

A25 Explain why Louise, and then why Paul, need mainly fast or slow twitch fibres or a mixture of each.

A26 Explain, using a sporting action, how Louise would use the antagonistic pairings of the biceps and triceps in hockey.

A27 Explain, using a sporting action, how Paul would use the antagonistic pairings of the quadriceps and hamstrings in rock climbing.

A28 Why would a build-up of muscle fatigue be more of a problem for Paul?

A29 Give an example of isotonic muscle action from Louise's sport.

A30 Give an example of isometric muscle action from Paul's sport.

7.1   THE HEART

● ● ● ● In this unit you will learn to identify the structure of the heart.

Your blood works non-stop, 24 hours a day. It carries food and oxygen to your body cells. It carries carbon dioxide and other waste away.

Blood is pumped round the body by the heart. It flows along tubes called **blood vessels**. The blood, heart and blood vessels together make up your **circulatory system**.

A FIRST LOOK AT THE CIRCULATORY SYSTEM

Below is a simple plan of your circulatory system. It shows just the heart and four main blood vessels:

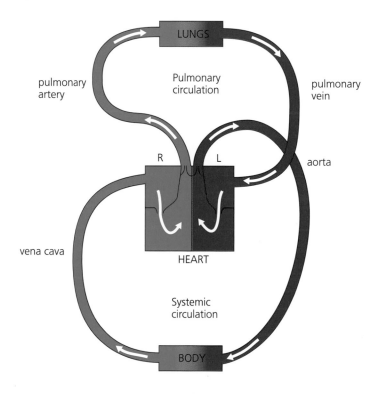

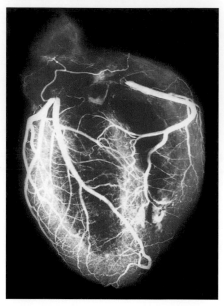

A heart treated with special dye to show up the arteries when x-rayed. This helps to spot heart disease and blockages.

◎ Notice how the heart is divided down the middle. Each part is a pump so the heart is a double pump for a double circulation.
◎ The right side pumps blood to the lungs and then it returns to the heart. This is called the **pulmonary circulation**.
◎ The left side pumps blood to the body and then it returns to the heart. This is called the **systemic circulation**.
◎ Try to learn the vena cava and aorta first. Once you have done this it will help you with the rest. The **A**orta is an **A**rtery and **A**rteries go **A**way from the heart. The **V**ena cava is a **V**ein and veins go towards the heart.
◎ Look at the diagram. Oxygen is picked up in the lungs and then transported to the body, passing through the heart on the way. Carbon dioxide does the opposite.

The heart has four hollows or *chambers* inside. The two upper chambers are called *atria*. Each is an atrium.

The two lower chambers are called *ventricles*.

The walls of the heart are made of *cardiac muscle*.

The wall down the middle is called the *septum*. It divides the heart into two parts.

Valves prevent back flow of blood. The two between the atria and the ventricles are the tricuspid and bicuspid valves and the ones between the heart and the arteries are semi-lunar (half-moon) valves.

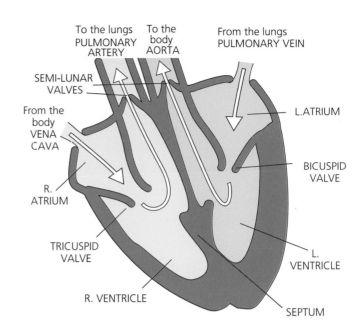

HOW THE HEART PUMPS BLOOD

The heart pumps blood by contracting. It does this in two stages.

First the atria contract. Then about a tenth of a second later the ventricles contract. This shows what happens:

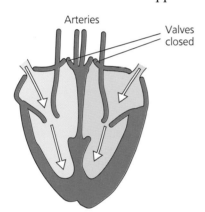

1 When the heart is relaxed, both sides fill with blood from the veins. (But no blood can flow in from the arteries. Can you see why?)

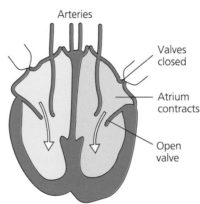

2 The atria contract. The veins contract where they join the atria. So blood from the atria is forced into the ventricles.

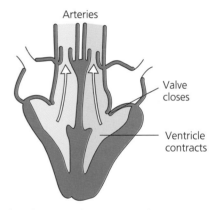

3 Then the ventricles contract. The valves between the ventricles and atria close. So the blood is forced out of the heart, into the arteries.

4 The heart muscle relaxes again and steps 1 – 3 are repeated.

QUESTIONS

1 What are the heart walls made of?

2 What are the two upper chambers called?

3 What are the two lower chambers called?

4 Where would you find **a** the bicuspid valve? **b** the tricuspid valve? **c** a semi-lunar valve?

5 A 'hole in the heart' baby has a hole through the septum allowing blood from the left and right sides to mix. Why is this such a problem?

6 What are the names of the two circulations?

7 What is the function of each?

Discussion work

8 You are running in your main sport. A molecule of blood has picked up oxygen in the lungs. With a partner, discuss the route it would take from here, round the circulatory system, and back to the lungs.

7.2 THE HEART AND EXERCISE

● ● ● ● In this unit you will learn how heart rate, stroke volume and cardiac output are affected by exercise.

There are three very important definitions you must learn: heart rate, stroke volume, and cardiac output.

Heart rate. This is the number of times your heart beats per minute.

At each heart beat, blood is pumped into your arteries. It makes the artery walls expand. Then they contract. One expansion and contraction is called a **pulse**.

You can feel pulses at several points in your body. By counting the pulses you can tell your heart rate.

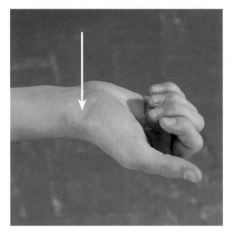

One **pulse point** is on the **carotid** artery in your neck, in the groove beside your windpipe. Either side will do! See if you can find it.

Another is on the **radial** artery at your wrist, below the thumb. To take your pulse, you need a watch with a seconds hand.

Press lightly on the pulse point with your first two fingers. Note the time. Start counting. Stop when a minute is up.

When we are at rest, the average heart rate is about 70 beats per minute (bpm). As soon as we start exercising, this rises. In extreme exercise it reaches its maximum (205 – at your age). This occurs because your body is desperate for oxygen and is trying to get rid of the poisonous carbon dioxide. This immediate rise is known as a short-term effect of exercise. A long-term effect is that your heart grows bigger and stronger (because it is a muscle). This is called hypertrophy. This means it can hold more blood and contract more strongly – in other words it has a bigger stroke volume.

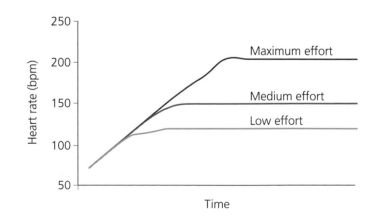

Stroke volume. This is the volume of blood pumped out of the heart by each ventricle during one contraction. At rest the heart chambers do not completely empty with every contraction. As soon as exercise starts, they fill more and empty more due to the heart contracting more strongly. As said on the previous page, a long-term effect of training causes hypertrophy and stroke volume increases.

This is how stroke volume increases during exercise:

◉ Contracting muscles squeeze on your veins, which causes more blood to squirt back into the heart.
◉ The heart gets fuller. That makes its fibres stretch more.
◉ Because its fibres are more stretched, the heart contracts more strongly
– just like when you stretch an elastic band. A stronger contraction forces out more blood.

Cardiac output. This is the amount of blood ejected from the heart in one minute. This can be explained in an equation:

heart rate x stroke volume = cardiac output
e.g. 70 bpm x 70ml = 4.9 l

In other words, at rest, nearly five litres of blood travels around your body. If we could get two identical people – one unfit and one fit – they would still need the same cardiac output at rest, i.e. 4.9 litres. However, remember the fit person will have a larger stroke volume.

Cardiac output = stroke volume x heart rate
unfit 4.9 l = 70ml x 70 bpm
fit 4.9 l = 90ml x 55 bpm

Look what happens – the fit person's heart does not have to beat as many times to supply the 4.9 litres. This means the fitter you are the slower your resting heart rate will be.

Now look what happens during maximum exercise for a fifteen-year-old:

stroke volume x heart rate = cardiac output
unfit = 120ml x 205 bpm = 24.6 l
fit = 150ml x 205 bpm = 30.8 l

The fit person has more blood travelling round the body, and therefore, more oxygen. They can keep going for longer.

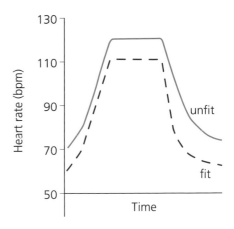

A graph of two people doing the same exercise at the same speed.
The fit person has:
* *a lower resting heart rate*
* *a lower heart rate during exercise*
* *recovers quicker, i.e. their heart rate returns to the resting level faster.*

AGE AND THE CARDIOVASCULAR SYSTEM

As you get older, your maximum heart rate drops, which means that your cardiac output is less. This means that intense exercise cannot be sustained for as long.

A good aerobic (endurance) based training programme can, up to the age of eighty, give the person an oxygen-transporting system similar to that of someone 20 years younger than themselves!

QUESTIONS

1 What are the immediate effects of exercise on your heart rate?

2 What are the two reasons that this happens?

3 The long-term effect of exercise on the heart is hypertrophy. How does this affect your resting heart rate?

4 Write out (using figures) how you would find this person's cardiac output. Paul went for a jog. His heart rate went up to 130 bpm and his stroke volume to 110ml.

Discussion work

5 Discuss how it would be possible for identical twins running at the same speed to have different heart rates.

7.3 BLOOD

In this unit you will learn the three types of blood vessel and how they help control our body temperature.

We have three different types of blood vessel:

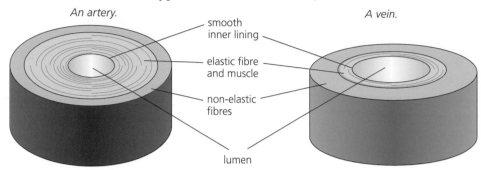

An artery.

smooth inner lining

elastic fibre and muscle

non-elastic fibres

lumen

A vein.

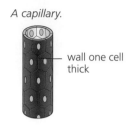

A capillary.

wall one cell thick

Arteries need a lot of elastic fibre and muscle to (a) cope with the surge of blood as it leaves the heart and (b) to change the lumen size when needed. Arteries and arterioles (see below) can become larger (**vasodilate**) or smaller (**vasoconstrict**). This means blood can be encouraged to enter some places and shut off from other places. During exercise little blood goes to the stomach but lots to the working muscles. This is called **vascular shunt**.

THE VALVES IN VEINS

By the time blood reaches the veins it is flowing more slowly, so at lower pressures veins have valves to make sure it can't flow backwards.

Many large veins are inside your leg and arm muscles. When the muscles contract, they squirt the blood towards your heart.

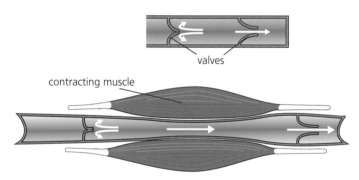

valves

contracting muscle

BLOOD VESSELS

1 The biggest artery – the aorta – swiftly divides into smaller arteries.
2 Arteries divide into smaller arterioles.
3 Arterioles divide into tiny capillaries that cover the muscle.
4 Capillaries join together to form the slightly larger venules (small veins).
5 Venules join together to form veins.
6 The largest vein enters the heart – the vena cava.

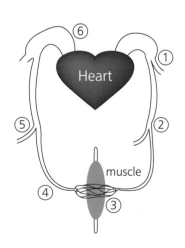

Heart

muscle

The differences between arteries and veins	
VEINS	ARTERIES
have valves	do not have valves
lead to the heart	go away from the heart
rarely pulsate	pulsate
blood flows under low pressure	blood flows under high pressure
have thin muscle and elastic tissue	have thick muscle and elastic tissue
mainly carry deoxygenated blood	mainly carry oxygenated blood

CONTROL OF TEMPERATURE

One of the major functions of our blood is to control temperature. Your body does not like change. Normally, your body temperature is 37°C and your blood is about 50% water. If you get too hot during exercise, or lose too much water in sweat, the body takes action to get back to normal.

IF YOU GET TOO HOT

Exercise makes you warm. This is because cell respiration in the muscles increases, giving out heat. Blood carries the heat around your body. But when your temperature starts to rise, this is what happens:

1 Blood vessels under the skin expand. This is called **vasodilation**. Now more blood flows near the surface. It loses heat by **radiation**. Just like a radiator!
2 The sweat glands make more sweat. This is mainly **water**. Heat from your body makes it **evaporate**, which helps to cool you.

When you exercise on a hot dry day or in a sports hall you can lose a lot of water as sweat. If the air is hot and humid, sweat will not evaporate. Your temperature may rise out of control. This is called **heat stroke** and it can kill you.

IF YOU GET TOO COOL

If your body temperature drops below 37°C, your body tries to stop it getting colder:
1 You stop sweating.
2 The blood vessels under the skin contract. This is called **vasoconstriction**. Now less blood flows near the surface so less heat is lost.
3 Your muscles may start to shiver. This produces heat.

But if you get cold enough, your reactions slow down. You lose control of your hands and you can't walk properly. You can't think straight. You are suffering from **hypothermia**. It can kill you.

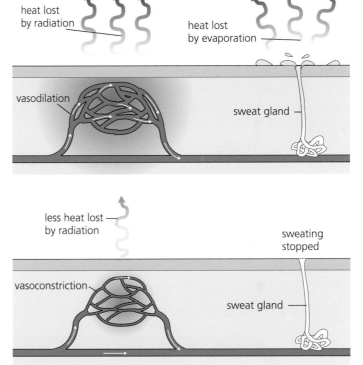

To be on top of our sporting performance we, therefore, need to control our temperature. Water intake is vital as we can lose up to three litres of sweat an hour. Lack of water can cause dehydration which makes you weak and dizzy.

QUESTIONS

1 Give two reasons why an artery has to have more elastic and muscle tissue than a vein.
2 Why do veins have valves?
3 In the differences between veins and arteries it says veins 'mainly' carry deoxygenated blood. One vein is different from the rest. Which one?

4 When doing mountain walking it is possible to get hypothermia. What is this?

Discussion work

5 You arrive at your sporting venue and feel freezing. By the time you are ten minutes into your sport you have warmed up. Discuss the changes that have been taking place in your blood vessels and blood.

7.4 WHAT'S IN BLOOD

• • • • • In this unit you will learn the functions of the blood cells.

Blood is a liquid called plasma, with red cells, white cells and platelets floating in it. You have nearly 5 litres of it in your body – enough to fill 8 or 9 milk bottles!

PLASMA

Plasma is a yellowish liquid. It is mostly water, with different things dissolved in it. The dissolved substances include:
◎ glucose and other nutrients from digested food
◎ hormones
◎ carbon dioxide and other waste from cells.

RED CELLS

Red cells are the body's oxygen carriers. They contain a red substance called haemoglobin which combines readily with oxygen. Haemoglobin gives the cells their red colour.

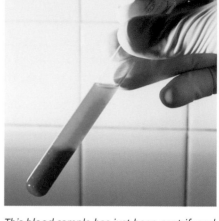

This blood sample has just been centrifuged. The yellow liquid is plasma. The red cells have collected at the bottom of the tube.

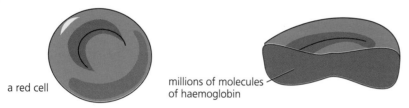

a red cell   millions of molecules of haemoglobin

The red cells are made in red marrow in some bones (mainly the ribs, vertebrae, humerus and femur). You have an enormous number of them: around 5 million in each drop of blood.

HOW RED CELLS CARRY OXYGEN

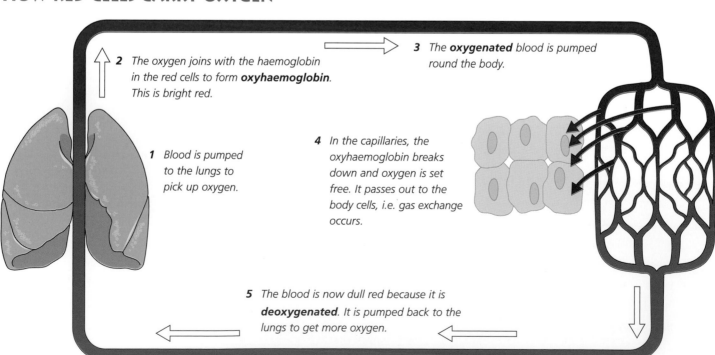

2 The oxygen joins with the haemoglobin in the red cells to form **oxyhaemoglobin**. This is bright red.

3 The **oxygenated** blood is pumped round the body.

1 Blood is pumped to the lungs to pick up oxygen.

4 In the capillaries, the oxyhaemoglobin breaks down and oxygen is set free. It passes out to the body cells, i.e. gas exchange occurs.

5 The blood is now dull red because it is **deoxygenated**. It is pumped back to the lungs to get more oxygen.

WHITE CELLS

White cells defend your body against disease. They are larger than red cells, and have a nucleus. There are several different kinds of white cell, all doing different jobs. For example white cells called **phagocytes** eat up germs:

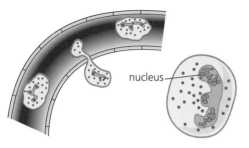

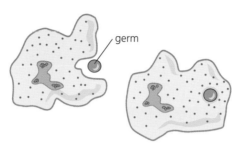

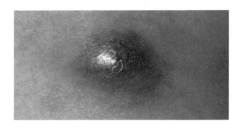

1 The phagocytes pass out through capillary walls and into the infected tissue.

2 They change shape to surround the germs. They produce enzymes to kill and digest them.

3 Phagocytes live for only a short time. Dead phagocytes, dead germs and liquid form pus in the infected area.

Other white cells make **antibodies**. These are chemicals that destroy germs. Different germs need different antibodies.

White cells are made in your red bone marrow, lymph nodes and spleen. Your blood has far fewer white cells than red ones. But when you are ill, more white cells are produced to help you fight infection.

PLATELETS

Platelets are fragments from special cells made in red bone marrow. They stick to each other easily. Their job is to stop your body losing blood. They do this by making the blood clot. This is how they work:

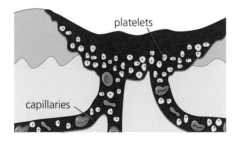

1 When you cut your hand, platelets stick to the surface of the wound and to each other.

2 They produce a substance that makes tiny fibres grow. Red cells get trapped in these. A clot forms.

3 The clot hardens to a scab, like on this head wound. It will drop off when new skin grows.

QUESTIONS

1 What is blood?

2 What is the main substance in plasma?

3 Name three other substances in plasma.

4 a What is the job of red cells? **b** What substance helps them do this job? **c** How does this substance work?

5 One kind of blood cell has a nucleus. Which one?

6 What is the job of white cells?

7 White cells called **phagocytes** eat up germs. Explain how they do this.

8 What are **antibodies**? What produces them?

Discussion work

9 You have fallen on a dirty court and grazed your knee. Discuss two ways in which your blood cells will help you heal.

7.5 WHAT BLOOD DOES

• • • • In this unit you will learn the overall function of blood.

Your blood has two jobs: to carry things around the body and to protect you against infection.

WHAT BLOOD CARRIES

Your blood is like a non-stop delivery service. It picks things up in one part of the body and carries them to another part.

	Blood carries	How
1	oxygen from the lungs to all your body cells	in red cells
2	carbon dioxide from the cells to the lungs for excretion	mainly in plasma
3	other waste, and excess water, from cells to the kidneys for excretion	in plasma
4	glucose and other nutrients from the gut to the cells	in plasma
5	hormones from the hormone glands to the parts that use them	in plasma
6	white blood cells to infected places	floating in plasma
7	heat from warmer to cooler parts of the body and to the skin for removal	all parts of the blood

HOW BLOOD PROTECTS YOU

Germs are **bacteria** and **viruses** that cause disease. They can enter your body through your lungs, through cuts, and in food and water. The platelets and white cells in blood protect you.

◎ Platelets cause blood to clot. This stops germs getting into cuts.
◎ If germs do get into your body, some white cells eat them up. Others make antibodies to destroy them.

If the germs are ones your white cells have not met before, it may take some time to make an antibody. But once they have done it, they can do it faster next time. If the germs return they are destroyed immediately. You become *immune* to the disease.

Immunization. The baby is being injected with a weak form of the bacteria that cause meningitis. Her white cells will develop antibodies, making her immune to the disease.

BLOOD PRESSURE

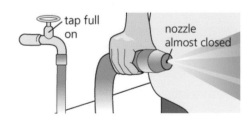

When the tap is full on, and the nozzle nearly closed, the water pressure in a hose is very high. High enough to damage plants.

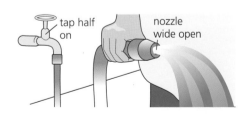

Now it is much lower. The pressure depends on how much water flows into the hose and how easily it can flow out.

Blood pressure is the same. It depends on how much blood flows into a blood vessel and how easily it can flow out.

That's why blood pressure is different in different blood vessels.

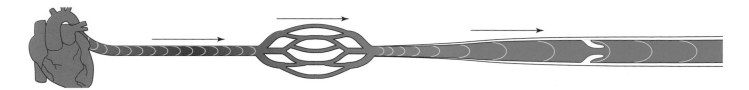

It is highest in the arteries. The blood pumps in fast, but it can't flow out through arterioles easily because they are so narrow.

It is lower in the capillaries, because the blood flows into them more slowly and then flows out to wider tubes.

It is lowest in the veins because the blood drains into them quite slowly and they are the widest blood vessels.

MEASURING BLOOD PRESSURE

Blood pressure is always measured at an artery in your arm. It is measured using a rubber cuff attached to a thin tube of mercury.

The blood pressure in the artery rises when your heart contracts and falls when it relaxes. Both values are measured. Normal blood pressure is around 120/80. You say this as 120 over 80. It means that the pressure is 120mm when the heart contracts and 80mm when it relaxes. (120mm and 80mm are the height of the mercury in the tube.)

BLOOD AND EXERCISE

Short-term effects

When you exercise, your heart beats faster and pumps out more blood, so your blood pressure rises. If it rises too much it is dangerous. Your body takes action to prevent this. For example, the brain sends a message to the arterioles to open wider. This reduces blood pressure. But it also helps you in another way. Now more blood gets to your muscles faster, carrying oxygen for respiration.

Long-term effects

Training results in more blood cells being produced and more capillaries being made, i.e. *increased capillarisation*.

This means that more oxygen can be carried and gas exchange can happen quicker and more efficiently.

Measuring blood pressure. The doctor pumps up the cuff until the pressure inside it just equals the pressure in the artery. He can tell by listening through the stethoscope. As the cuff is pumped up, the mercury rises in the tube.

QUESTIONS

1 Why is blood pressure highest in arteries?

2 Explain why blood pressure is lowest in veins.

3 Where in the body is blood pressure measured?

4 If you cut an artery the blood pumps out in spurts. If you cut a vein it seeps out steadily. Try to explain this difference.

5 Name two things carried in blood: **a** which are gases (how does the blood carry them?) **b** which the body will excrete.

6 What are germs?

7 Name two things in blood that protect you.

8 If you catch measles once, you won't catch it again. Explain why?

Discussion work

9 Discuss the short-term and long-term ways in which your body tries to supply more blood to the working muscles.

QUESTIONS ON CHAPTER 7

Question hints: the heart and circulation

To answer questions about the heart and circulation, start by scribbling a diagram like this.

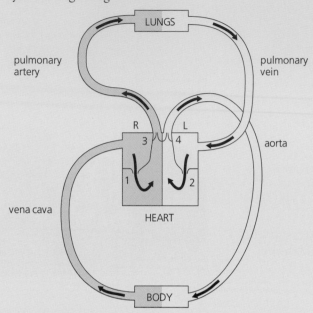

1 First draw a square box for the heart. Now draw a line down the middle to represent the septum. Mark the two halves **R** and **L** for right and left. (You are facing the drawing so **R** is on your left!)

2 Draw two more boxes, for the body and lungs.

3 Draw in the blood vessels and direction of blood flow. Remember, it flows out beside the septum.

R → lungs → side of L (Ron loves London)

L → body → side of R (Lessons bore Ron)

4 Label the blood vessels. Remember:
- **arteries** carry blood away from the heart.
- veins carry blood to it.
- the main artery from the heart is the **aorta**.
- the main vein to it is the **vena cava**.
- **pulmonary** means to do with the lungs.

5 Now draw in the four valves in the heart.
- 1 and 2 separate the upper and lower chambers of the heart. They are the **cuspid** valves.
  - 1 is called the **tricuspid** valve.
  - 2 is called the **bicuspid** or **mitral** valve.
- 3 and 4 lead out of the heart.
  - They are the **semi-lunar** valves.

6 The upper chambers of the heart are the **atria**. The lower chambers are the **ventricles**. Write these labels on.

---

1 Scribble a simple diagram of the heart and circulation by following the instructions on the left.
Practise until you can do it in less than 2 minutes.

2 On a scribble diagram from 1:
a shade the oxygenated blood red
b shade the deoxygenated blood blue.

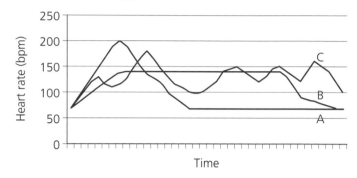

3 which of the above heart rates do you think belongs to:
a a 100-metre sprinter?
b a long-distance runner?
c a games player?
Give reasons for your answers.

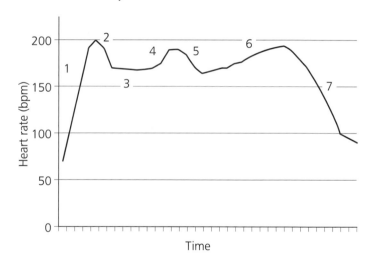

4 The above graph is the heart rate for a 10 000-metre runner. Match each statement to a correct number.
a The race settled into a steady pace.
b At the beginning of the race there was a sprint to gain position.
c A sudden burst of speed left most of the other runners behind.
d The pace increased during the last lap.

5 Anjou goes for a run at a gentle pace. What would be the immediate effects upon her heart? Use this equation to help you:

$$\text{stroke volume} \times \text{heart rate} = \text{cardiac output}$$

If she trained regularly, what long-term effects would change the above equation at rest?

6 If Anjou trained regularly, her maximum cardiac output would be greater than before she started her training. Why?

7 In many sports you see on TV you may have noticed people run on with drinks bottles during every stoppage. What do you think the effect of too little fluid would be?

8 List two sports, apart from mountain walking, where hypothermia could affect you.

9 What is the ideal body temperature?

10 Explain the two things that the body does to try to keep cool.

11 Explain the three things that the body does to try to keep warm.

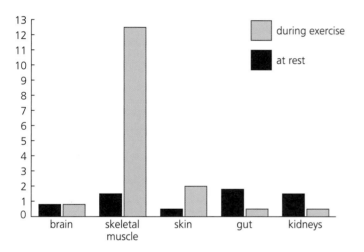

12 The above diagram shows how the blood flow to different parts of the body changes during exercise.
  a Explain how and why exercise affects blood flow to:
    i your skin
    ii your muscles
    iii your gut
    iv your kidneys
  b Blood flow to the brain is undisturbed by exercise. Why is this important?

APPLIED QUESTIONS

Connie is a fit, county standard football midfielder. She is 17 years old and is currently taking her A levels. She has recently suffered from a twisted (sprained) ankle and has been out of training for a month. She trains on her own most days, but has club training on Tuesdays and matches on Saturdays.

A13 Give reasons that might explain why Connie's resting heart rate is 55 bpm? (2 marks)

A14 Give reasons that might explain why, despite doing the same training and exercise as her friend, Michael, he can perform better when they do a long training run? (3 marks)

A15 Connie will perform aerobic and anaerobic training to improve her cardiovascular system. Give reasons that might explain why a larger heart and heart wall will allow Connie to perform better in matches. (2 marks)

A16 Connie often performs a skills circuit at Tuesday's club training session. Give reasons why this might benefit her performance in matches. (2 marks)

A17 Connie's coach decides he wants to test the group's aerobic fitness. Name and briefly describe a test that will do this. (3 marks)

A18 Below is a graph of Connie's heart rate on a training run before and after her ankle injury. She went at the same speed/intensity for them both. With reference to the relevant principle of training, can you explain why the one after the injury is different in:
  • resting heart rate
  • her heart rate when working
  • recovery time.
      (4 marks)

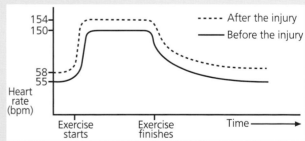

A19 As a games player Connie needs to improve many aspects of fitness.
  • Name three important ones. (3 marks)
  • Choose one and briefly describe the training method used to improve it for Connie. (5 marks)
  • What principals of training would she need to consider? (6 marks)

8.1 THE RESPIRATORY SYSTEM

• • • • In this unit you will learn the mechanism of breathing and the long-term effects of exercise on it.

THE RESPIRATORY SYSTEM

Your cells obtain energy by aerobic respiration. That needs oxygen. Your body takes it from the air via the respiratory system. Below is a diagram showing the passage of air into your lungs.

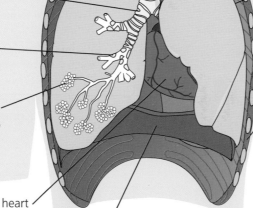

Air is drawn in through the nose, where it is filtered by tiny hairs and warmed and moistened by **mucus**.

The voice box or **larynx**, which makes sounds for speaking.

The windpipe or **trachea**. This is a flexible tube held open by rings of cartilage.

In the lungs, the trachea branches into two **bronchi**. Each is a bronchus.

The bronchi branch into smaller tubes called **bronchioles**.

The bronchioles end in bunches of tiny air sacs called **alveoli**. Their walls are so thin that gases can pass through them.

A small flap of cartilage stops food going into the windpipe instead of the gullet. It is called the **epiglottis**.

The **lungs** are soft and spongy.

The lungs are in a space called the **thoracic cavity**.

The **pleural membrane** is a slippery skin lining the cavity. It protects the lungs as they rub against the ribs.

The **ribs** protect the lungs.

The **intercostal muscles** between the ribs help you breathe in and out.

heart

The **diaphragm** is a sheet of muscle below the lungs. It helps you breathe in and out.

HOW MUCH AIR DO YOU BREATHE?

◎ The **tidal volume** is the amount of air you breathe in or out with each breath. When you exercise it increases.

◎ **Respiratory rate** is how many breaths you take in a minute. Once again this rises as a short-term effect of exercise.

◎ The **vital capacity** is the maximum amount of air you can breathe out, after breathing in as deeply as you can. It is usually around 4.5 or 5 litres. It is very important to sports people as the more air you can get rid of in the first few seconds the less carbon dioxide is left in you.

Tidal volume x respiratory rate = minute volume

i.e. the amount you breathe per minute

BREATHING AND EXERCISE

Breathing is also called **external respiration** or just **respiration**.
Don't confuse it with cell respiration (as described in the next unit)!
Breathing in is **inspiration**.
Breathing out is **expiration**.

WHEN YOU BREATHE IN

several changes take place.

1 *The intercostal muscles contract. This pulls the rib cage upwards. So the chest expands.*

2 *The diaphragm contracts. This pulls it down and flattens it, making the chest even larger.*

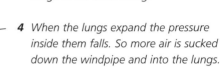

3 *When the chest expands, the lungs expand too, because their moist surface clings to the chest lining.*

4 *When the lungs expand the pressure inside them falls. So more air is sucked down the windpipe and into the lungs.*

WHEN YOU BREATHE OUT

the opposite changes take place.

1 *The intercostal muscles relax. This lowers the rib cage and makes the chest smaller.*

2 *The diaphragm relaxes so it bulges upwards again. This makes the chest even smaller.*

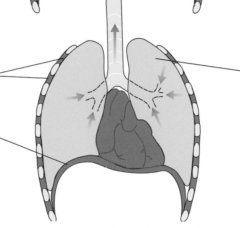

3 *When the chest gets smaller the lungs are compressed. So air is pushed out of the lungs and up the windpipe.*

When you exercise, these muscles contract more strongly and more often to get more air in and more carbon dioxide out.

EFFECTS OF TRAINING

◎ Your breathing muscles (intercostals and diaphragm) grow stronger which allows deeper breaths, i.e. your vital capacity increases.
◎ More alveoli become surrounded with capillaries so gas exchange is more efficient.
◎ The joint effect of this is that aerobic/stamina work can continue longer before you tire.

QUESTIONS

1 What are the proper terms for breathing in and out?
2 Between what two structures does gas exchange take place?
3 What is another name for breathing?
4 When you breathe in your chest expands, **a** explain how this happens, **b** explain why your lungs expand too?

Discussion work

5 With reference to your main sport, explain how the effects of training the respiratory system will delay the build-up of lactic acid.

8.2 EFFECTS OF EXERCISE ON THE RESPIRATORY SYSTEM

● ● ● ● In this unit you will learn about gas exchange during rest and exercise.

Remember unit 2.3 on energy systems. Even at rest we still need oxygen because our cardiac and smooth muscles are working constantly, as are our breathing muscles.

We have looked at the mechanism that brings air in and now we will look in greater detail at how the gases are exchanged between our lungs and capillaries.

THE ALVEOLI

Your lungs take in oxygen and give out carbon dioxide. This gas exchange takes place between the alveoli of the lungs (see below) and capillaries.

These are the alveoli at the end of a bronchiole. Each is smaller than a grain of salt.

The alveoli are covered with tiny blood vessels called **capillaries**. Gases can pass through the capillary walls.

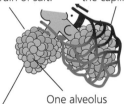

One alveolus

The walls of the alveoli are thin and moist, which helps gases pass through.

GAS EXCHANGE IN THE ALVEOLI

The diagram opposite shows what happens in the alveoli.

3 The carbon dioxide travels out of the lungs and up the windpipe. You breathe it out.

1 Blood carries waste carbon dioxide from the body cells to the alveoli.

carbon dioxide out

oxygen in

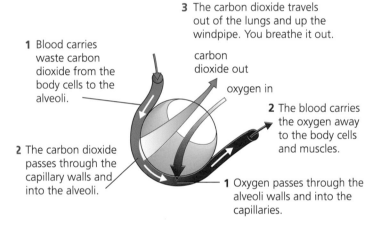

2 The blood carries the oxygen away to the body cells and muscles.

2 The carbon dioxide passes through the capillary walls and into the alveoli.

1 Oxygen passes through the alveoli walls and into the capillaries.

HOW AIR CHANGES IN YOUR LUNGS

In the lungs, oxygen is taken from air and carbon dioxide added to it. So the air you breathe out is different from the air you breathe in.

This table shows the changes:

Substance	Amount in inhaled air (the air you breathe in)	Amount in exhaled air (the air you breathe out)
oxygen	21%	17%
carbon dioxide	a tiny amount	3%
nitrogen	79%	79%
water	little	more

Look at nitrogen. The amount does not change. Can you explain why?

CHANGES DURING EXERCISE

Remember how energy is made aerobically (with oxygen) at rest:

$$\text{Glucose (or fat)} + O_2 \rightarrow \text{energy} + H_2O + CO_2$$

This means that if your exhaled air was collected while you were exercising there would be less oxygen in it. This is because it has been used up in the muscles to supply the extra energy you now need. The harder the exercise, the more energy you need and the more oxygen you use. Therefore you will breathe out less oxygen.

The opposite occurs with carbon dioxide and water. They are the waste products made when energy is produced. Therefore the harder the work, the more energy is needed and so more carbon dioxide and water are made. Exhaled air will have more of these.

YOUR LUNGS AND EXERCISE

Your lungs and heart work as a team to get oxygen round the body and clear carbon dioxide away. When you exercise, your heart and lungs have to work harder. This is what happens:

1 During exercise, cell respiration in your muscles increases, so the level of carbon dioxide in your blood rises.

2 Your brain detects this. It sends a signal to your lungs to breathe faster and deeper.

4 The brain also sends a signal to your heart to beat faster, so:
– more blood gets pumped to the lungs for gas exchange
– more blood gets pumped to the muscles, carrying oxygen and removing carbon dioxide.

3 Gas exchange in your lungs speeds up. More carbon dioxide passes out of the blood and more oxygen passes into it.

Look how breathing changes during exercise:

For an 18-year-old...	at rest	during exercise
tidal volume	0.5 litres	2.5 litres
respiratory rate	12 breaths a minute	30 breaths a minute
minute volume	6 litres a minute	75 litres a minute

QUESTIONS

1 What two gases are exchanged in the lungs?

2 The alveoli have very thin walls. Why do you think this is useful?

3 You breathe out the same amount of nitrogen as you breathe in. Why is this?

4 In the table above, how did exercise change: **a** the tidal volume? **b** the respiratory rate? **c** the minute volume?

5 Explain how these changes helped the person.

Discussion work

6 Discuss why gas exchange may be less efficient **a** at altitude and **b** after smoking a cigarette.

8.3 SUMMARY OF TRAINING EFFECTS

● ● ● ● In this unit you will learn the long-term effects of exercise on the body.

In all the chapters so far we have looked at the changes that months of training can make to your body. We summarise them here.

THE EFFECTS OF AEROBIC TRAINING

1 On the heart and circulation. Over months of swimming or jogging or cycling these changes take place:

◎ Your heart grows bigger. It holds more blood and contracts more strongly. More blood gets pumped out with each heart beat. It becomes a more efficient pump.

This champion swimmer has a larger heart, more blood, more capillaries, and a greater lung capacity than he had when he started training.

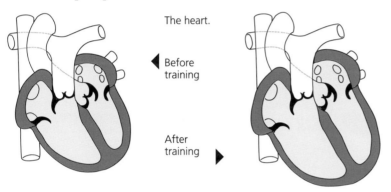

The heart.

◀ Before training

After training ▶

◎ Your resting heart rate falls, because now you can supply the same amount of blood with fewer heart beats. The fitter you are, the lower your resting heart rate.
◎ After exercise, your heart rate returns to its normal resting rate faster than it did before.
◎ The volume of blood in your body increases. You produce more red cells and more haemoglobin to help with oxygen delivery.
◎ Arteries grow larger and more elastic so blood pressure falls.

2 On the respiratory system. Aerobic training also increases the fitness of your lungs and respiratory system.
◎ The rib muscles and diaphragm grow stronger so the chest cavity gets bigger when you breathe in. This means the lungs can expand further, taking in more air with each breath.
◎ Since the lungs expand further, more alveoli are available for gas exchange. More oxygen can be picked up at each breath and more carbon dioxide removed.
◎ More capillaries grow around the alveoli, which means more blood gets carried to them.
◎ This means you can move oxygen to the muscles faster and get rid of carbon dioxide more quickly. This means you will not get tired so soon.

The combined effects of aerobic training on the heart, and the circulatory and respiratory systems is that your maximal oxygen consumption increases. This means that each kilogram of your body weight can process more oxygen which means exercise can continue for longer.

Capillaries around the alveoli.

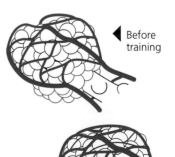

◀ Before training

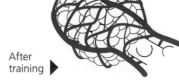

After training ▶

THE EFFECTS OF ANAEROBIC TRAINING

Anaerobic training has these effects:

◎ Your heart walls get thicker to cope with the strain of all-out effort on your circulation system. Especially the left ventricle wall.
◎ Your muscles are able to tolerate lactic acid better and clear it away faster. This means you can go all out for longer than before.

THE EFFECTS OF MUSCLE TRAINING

Endurance training. Endurance training has these effects on muscles:

◎ They get better at using oxygen, so they can work harder for longer without fatigue.
◎ They get better at using fat for energy. This is good since your body has lots of stored fat. It gives more energy than glycogen per gram.
◎ More capillaries grow around the muscles so more blood reaches them, bringing oxygen and food and removing carbon dioxide.

Strength training. Strength training has these effects on muscles:

◎ They grow thicker, because the muscle fibres grow thicker.
An increase in muscle size and strength is called **hypertrophy**.
◎ They contract more strongly and efficiently.
◎ The tendons get bigger and stronger.

THE EFFECT ON BONES

As you saw in chapter 5, bones are alive. Cells called **osteoblasts** build new bone while cells called osteoclasts break it down again. All training puts extra stress on your bones. This makes the osteoblasts work harder so your bones get stronger.

THE EFFECTS ON JOINTS

◎ Exercise makes ligaments stronger.
◎ It also thickens the cartilage at joints, so bones are better at absorbing shock.
◎ Stretching increases the range of movement at a joint, and helps muscles contract more strongly.

THE EFFECTS ON BODY FAT

◎ Training increases your basal metabolic rate. You burn up stored fat faster even when you are resting.
◎ Since your muscles get better at using fat for energy, more fat is burned up during exercise too. So you get slimmer.

Endurance training has no effect on the size of your muscles. It takes strength training with heavy weights to enlarge them like this.

ALTITUDE TRAINING

Training in a very high place, e.g. Mexico City causes a problem for distance runners. There is less oxygen in every breath. Training at altitude makes the aerobic changes on the previous page happen quicker.

It is good for anaerobic events as there is less gas to push your way through. You can jump and throw further and sprint faster.

QUESTIONS

1 How would you expect these to change over months of jogging: **a** your resting heart rate **b** your lung volume **c** your rib muscles **d** your leg bones **e** the cartilage at your knee joints?

2 It takes all-out effort to lift heavy weights. So the muscles work anaerobically. What long-term effect will this have on the weightlifter's heart?

3 Training reduces body fat in two ways. What are they?

Discussion work

4 Name one of your sports and then discuss the long-term effects of exercise on your body if you had trained for a year.

QUESTIONS ON CHAPTER 8

1 Look at this table:

	% oxygen	% carbon dioxide
Inhaled air	21	0.03
Exhaled air during quiet breathing	17	3
Exhaled air during exercise	15	6

  a Why is there less oxygen in exhaled air than in inhaled air?

  b Why is there more carbon dioxide in exhaled air than in inhaled air?

  c Explain why the percentage of oxygen in exhaled air falls during exercise.

  d Explain why the percentage of carbon dioxide in exhaled air rises during exercise.

  e Exhaled air contains at least 15% oxygen. Explain why this makes the 'kiss-of-life' possible.

2 A spirometer was used to record an athlete's breathing at rest and after exercise. Each wave (from one trough to the next) represents one breath. From the height of the wave you can tell the volume of air breathed in.

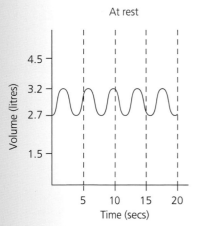
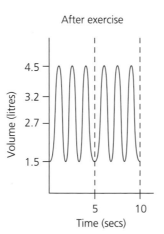

  a What was the athlete's tidal volume at rest?

  b What was her tidal volume after exercise?

  c What was her respiratory rate:

    i at rest?

    ii after exercise?

3 Exhaled air during exercise still contains at least 15% oxygen. Why does our breathing rate and tidal volume increase when we obviously do not require more air?

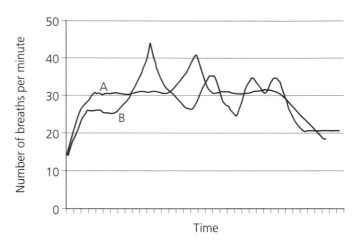

4 a Which of the above lines do you think is the long-distance runner and which the netball player? Give reasons for your answers.

  b Can you explain why the runner might have had the sudden change in heart rate?

Answer **either c** or **d** below

  c The netball player is a centre. Can you think of another position where the breathing rate would be very different and why?

  d If the graph were for two football players what difference would you expect to see between a striker and a midfielder?

5 Jack started a game of basketball.

  a Is it aerobic, anaerobic or both? Explain your answer using specific examples from a game.

His breathing got deeper and faster during the first few minutes.

  b Explain the mechanics of how he breathes.

  c What are the proper terms for:

    i the number of breaths he takes per minute.

    ii the amount he breathes in and out in one breath.

  d Jack's vital capacity is 5 litres. He can breathe out 80% of this in the first second. His friend, David, has asthma and when affected by it his air passages swell. He can only breathe out 40% of his vital capacity in the first second. Why do you think that this could be a problem?

Below is a graph of Jack's exercise and an explanation of what he is doing. Once you have read it answer the question below the graph.

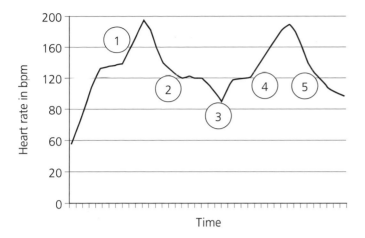

1: Twenty seconds of man-to-man defending, fast break and lay up.

2: Jogging while a team-mate has the ball.

3: Time out.

4: Jogging then very hard defending for the last thirty seconds of the game.

5: Game over.

6 Using the above graph and your information on oxygen debt, explain fully when one is created and when it can be partly or fully repaid.

7 What is produced in Jack's body that acts as a trigger for his brain to speed up his heart rate and breathing?

8 After several months of training Jack found that he could continue for longer before tiring. What long-term effects of training on his lungs would have helped to contribute to this?

APPLIED QUESTIONS

Jemma is three-quarters of the way through a marathon. She has just had to chase down a small group of runners who had broken away from the pack. She catches them but as they go up the next hill her legs really begin to ache and feel tired.

A9 Why did Jemma's breathing rate have to speed up when she tried to catch up the others?

A10 Jemma can take bigger breaths than she used to before she started training years ago. Why is this?

A11 Explain, using an equation, the type of energy production for most of the marathon.

A12 Explain, using an equation, the type of energy production for when Jemma moved up to a high speed to catch the others.

A13 What would be the long-term training effects on Jemma's heart?

A14 Why would she be able to exchange gases better than an untrained person?

A15 What types of training could Jemma do to improve her aerobic capacity?

A16 When training, what would you recommend Jemma's heart rate target zone should be and why?

A17 In this marathon Jemma could create an oxygen debt in three different ways, what are they?

A18 How could this affect her finish?

9.1   SKILL IN SPORT

• • • • In this unit you will learn what we mean by 'skill' and what is needed to produce a skilful performance.

When you watch top-level sport you are seeing the result of a lot of hard work from people who have a natural ability for that sport. They make it look easy. This has been achieved by a combination of *skill* and *ability*. But what do those terms mean?

SKILL

Skill is *learned*. You are not born with it and you can improve it with practice. It is **pre-determined** so you have an aim that you set out to achieve, for example performing a smash in badminton. When you perform skilfully your movements look co-ordinated, fluent and aesthetic. This means your movements are controlled, well-timed, fit smoothly together and look pleasing to watch. An unskilled performance may look jerky and awkward or even clumsy. Your performance will also be efficient, which means that you won't waste energy or time doing it.

Skill at batting in cricket means you have full control of your body and the bat. You choose the right shot to play and you perform it well each time. You are skilful.

ABILITY

Learning skills is only possible if you have the right abilities. Once the learning is done your *performance* will be skilful. Ability is something you are born with and for sport you need abilities like speed, agility, co-ordination, flexibility, balance and strength amongst others. You learned about these on pages 12–13.

If you want to be a good sprinter like Christine Ohuruogu, you need to have been born with very good potential for speed, power and a fast reaction time. Top gymnasts, however, need a lot of flexibility, balance, agility and co-ordination amongst their abilities.

OPEN AND CLOSED SKILLS

An **open skill** is one where your movements vary, depending on what is going on around you. It depends on your *environment*. For example on where your opponent is (netball) or the wind direction (sailing).

A **closed skill** is one where the movements are always exactly the same. They do not change with the environment. For the tennis serve, the sequence of movements is closed. But the timing and placing of the shot depend on the position of the player and his opponent. In that respect the serve is open.

What abilities are required to perform this skill?

*A goalkeeper saving a goal. This is an **open skill**. His move depends on where the ball is coming from. So next time it will be different.*

*A gymnast performing a backflip. This is a **closed skill**. She will repeat it exactly next time. Her environment is stable and does not affect her.*

Look at this tennis serve. Next time the player will repeat the moves but change the timing and placing of the shot. So is the skill closed or open?

You can place a skill between closed and open on a continuous scale or **continuum**.

Most motor skills, and sports, lie somewhere between closed and open. Hooking the ball in a rugby scrum is another example.

WHAT DOES A SKILFUL PERFORMANCE LOOK LIKE?

In your next PE lesson try and look at two people performing the same skill, one of whom is a beginner, the other a skilful performer. What do you imagine the differences will be between the two?

As a beginner or a novice you will make a lot of mistakes as you learn. Your performance will, therefore, be inconsistent. You may waste a lot of energy and you may take a long time to perform the skill. As a skilful performer, however, you will have learned the skill and so you will be able to repeat it frequently, you will be efficient with energy and time. Being skilful also means that you will be able to adapt within your game. A novice often does not fully understand the game situation and whilst they may be able to perform individual skills, they do not do as well when they are in a game and have to think and play. As a skilled performer you will be able to adapt your game as you go and select the right skills to suit the situation.

QUESTIONS

1 Take one of your practical activities. List the abilities required to become skilful in this activity.

2 Explain why swimming is a closed skill.

3 Why is making a pass in football an open skill?

4 Can you think of a sport in which closed skills are used in an open situation?

Discussion work

5 Imagine you are watching two people perform a tennis serve but one is a novice and the other a top performer. What differences would you expect to see between the two? Now apply this to a skill in your sport.

9.2 INFORMATION PROCESSING

● ● ● ● In this unit you will learn how the brain makes sense of the information it receives.

Whether you're playing tennis or throwing the discus or washing the dishes, your brain is in control. It processes information from your eyes, ears, skin and muscles, then tells your muscles what to do.

THE INFORMATION PROCESSING MODEL

This diagram shows the stages in processing information:

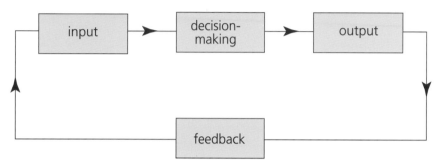

The information processing system.

INPUT

Input means the information you receive from your senses. In sport you get information through your eyes and ears. For example, in tennis you see your opponent hitting the ball and hear the thwack. But that's not all. You also feel a lot of information within your body. For example, how hard you are holding the racket and the position of your limbs.

DECISION-MAKING

Next your brain must decide how to respond to the input. The decision will have a big effect on the quality of your performance. Decision-making involves *perception* and *memory*.

Perception. This is the process of *interpreting* information. Suppose your opponent lobs the ball towards you. From what you hear and see and feel, your brain will judge:

◎ how hard the ball was struck
◎ how fast it is moving
◎ where and when it will arrive
◎ where your opponent will be standing by then
◎ how prepared you are.

Then it decides how you should respond. But it can't do any of this without memory.
Memory. Your memory has two parts: short-term and long-term.

Short-term memory is your 'work space'. All the information you receive goes in there. It stays only a short time – about two minutes at

If you've never seen a tennis ball before, you won't know how hard to hit it. There's nothing stored in your memory to help your brain make decisions.

most. If you ignore it, it fades very quickly. Paying attention holds it for longer. By concentrating you can transfer it to your long-term memory.

Long-term memory is your 'library'. It holds images, tastes, sounds, smells, feelings and actions you are familiar with, and all the sports skills you have learned and practised. It can hold a limitless amount of information, and store it for a lifetime.

If you have learned your tennis well and practised a lot, your long-term memory will have all you need for interpreting the information you receive during performance, plus programmes of instructions for action.

Selective attention. A great deal of information arrives in your short-term memory at one time. Your brain ignores most of it and concentrates on what seems important. This is called selective attention. When you are learning a skill you need to concentrate on each movement to get it right. But once you are more skilled you can concentrate on other things, such as the position of your opponent or the choice of shot to use. It is something you can improve with practice.

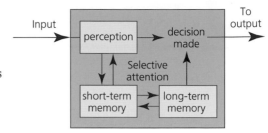

Decision-making.

OUTPUT

This is the action you take as a result of your brain's decision. For example you might play a drop shot. If your information processing is working well, and your long-term memory is well stocked with skills, your output is likely to be successful.

FEEDBACK

Feedback is the response you receive to your output. It tells you whether the output was successful or not. For example:

◎ you can usually feel whether a shot was good or bad
◎ the score changes
◎ your opponent misses the shot
◎ if it's a practice match, your coach may say something to you.

Note that in the information processing system model an arrow goes from **feedback** to **input**, completing the loop. Feedback becomes part of input. It will affect your next decision. Feedback from your coach helps you learn and improve. You will find out more about this on pages 124–125.

Selective attention is needed to ignore the shouts of the crowd and concentrate on the match.

QUESTIONS

1 Draw a simple diagram to show how you process information when playing your sport.

2 If you are just starting tennis, you probably won't play very well. Why?

3 What is: **a** output? **b** feedback? Give two examples of each from your sport.

4 What is *perception*? How is it linked to memory?

5 Think of a single skill in your sport. Describe how this skill is performed using the stages of the information processing model.

Discussion work

6 Discuss the importance of selective attention when:
a learning a new skill, **b** performing in a match.

9.3 LEARNING A NEW SKILL

In this unit you will learn about the types of guidance and practice that will help you to learn a new skill.

HOW TO LEARN A NEW SKILL

You could learn a new skill by trial and error but this is usually not the best way. A coach will be able to help you learn as they will be able to give you guidance and optimise your practice. It is useful to remember the information processing model and how it works (see 9.2) before you start to learn a new skill or coach someone else.

- Your information processing system can process only a limited amount of information at a time. Try to do too much and it will become confused.
- This means you learn best when there are no distractions. Remember selective attention?
- It also means you shouldn't try to learn too much at once. If you tried to learn a dance routine all at once you probably wouldn't succeed. The best way is to break it into parts and learn each separately.
- To help avoid confusion, instructions from your coach should be clear, simple and to the point.
- The instructions should concentrate on the most important aspects of the skill at first. Your brain will focus on these through selective attention.
- When your coach demonstrates a new skill, it goes into your short-term memory. Learning it means moving it into your long-term memory. You do this by practice.
- Your long-term memory can hold an almost limitless amount of information, and it is permanent. Once you have learned to swim or ride a bike you do not forget, although you may feel 'rusty'.

TYPES OF PRACTICE

You have to practise a new skill many times before you've really learned it. The best way to practise depends on the skill.

- If it's a basic skill such as catching a netball, you can practise the whole skill. This is called *whole practice*. Then you can move on to practise it within a netball game.
- If it's a complex skill, you should watch someone perform it first, and perhaps even try it out, to get a feeling for it. Then break it down and practise it in parts. This is called *part practice*. For example with a tennis serve you could practise the toss, then the swing and so on. Then put the parts together and practise the whole skill. And finally, try it in a game of tennis.
- When you're practising an open skill, for example dribbling a basketball, you should practise it in lots of different situations. This is called *variable practice*. It is important because your movements in an open skill will vary, depending on the environment.
- When you're practising a closed skill, keep repeating it under the same conditions. This is called *fixed practice*.

The lay-up shot in basketball is a complex skill that lends itself to part practice.

◎ When you are practising a skill within a game, it is usually best to work in small groups to begin with. This way you won't have to pay attention to too many other players, which might confuse you.

TYPES OF GUIDANCE

When you are learning and practising a skill, you usually need help or guidance from a teacher, coach or friend. This becomes *input* for your information processing system.

There are three types of guidance: *visual*, *verbal* and *manual* or mechanical. A good coach will use more than one kind.

Visual guidance. This is guidance you can see: demonstrations, DVDs, posters and wall charts. Visual guidance is especially useful when you are just starting to learn a new skill as it helps give you a picture in your mind of what you are trying to learn.

Verbal guidance. This is guidance you can *listen* to. The coach explains in words what you should do. It is useful because he or she can explain on the spot, repeat the instructions as often as needed, and tailor them to suit you.

Manual/mechanical guidance. This is guidance you can *feel*, where:

◎ the coach takes hold of you and guides you through the movement, for example a difficult dance routine (manual)
◎ or a device is used to restrict your movement and keep you safe, for example a swimming float or a tight safety rope when rock climbing (mechanical).

Manual guidance is useful where a skill is very complex, or dangerous, or you are scared. It gets you used to the movements of the skill before you try them out on your own.

Guidance is also a type of feedback, as you will see in the next unit. It not only gives you instructions about what to do but also informs you of what you have done.

Verbal guidance alone may be confusing or hard to understand. It is often best to combine it with manual or visual guidance.

1 What is part practice? When is it useful?

2 After part practice it is important to put the parts together and do whole practice. Why?

3 When is it best to use variable practice?

4 When is it best to use fixed practice?

5 Name and describe three types of guidance.

6 For each type of guidance, try to think of: **a** two advantages **b** two disadvantages.

7 Why might verbal guidance on its own be confusing?

Discussion work

8 Why is it important to use different types of practice and how is this linked to whether a skill is open or closed? What type of practice would you use if your sport required closed skills to be performed in an open situation?

9.4 TYPES OF FEEDBACK

● ● ● ● In this unit you will learn about the different types of feedback and their importance.

INTRINSIC FEEDBACK

Intrinsic means it is internal. It comes from something called **proprioception**. Information from your muscles, joints, skin and the organs that control balance tell you about the performance you have just made. Sometimes when you hit a ball you can tell from the feel of it that it was a really good shot. This is proprioception at work and this is the basis of intrinsic feedback. The opposite is also true. Sometimes you can feel if you have made a mistake or need to adjust something. Again the intrinsic feedback is telling you about your performance.

If you try to stand on one leg you will notice that you probably make minor adjustments with your muscles to try and hold your balance. You are receiving intrinsic feedback and using it to alter your position and prevent yourself from falling over. Have a go!

A lot of intrinsic feedback is ignored by a novice as they often do not recognise it and do not yet understand how to use it.

EXTRINSIC FEEDBACK

Extrinsic means external. In other words this feedback comes from outside sources. You can often *see* the results of your performance, e.g. when the ball goes into the basket or misses. If you do score, the crowd and your team-mates may congratulate you and you will *hear* this. If you are in a practice session with your coach, he or she may give you information about how well you are doing or offer advice on how to improve. All of this is extrinsic feedback.

Try and teach a friend a simple skill. You will probably try to help them by telling them what they have done right, what was wrong with their performance and how to improve it. All of this is extrinsic feedback.

KNOWLEDGE OF PERFORMANCE

Knowledge of performance (KP) tells you how well, or badly, you performed. For example how smooth your serve was, or your somersault.

◉ Some KP comes from proprioception – your own body awareness. You can feel how hard you hit a shot or kick a ball.
◉ Your coach and friends will provide KP.
◉ Recording your performance on video, and watching it later with your coach, is a good way to obtain KP.

The only way that this gymnast knows that her leg is straight is through proprioception.

If you're a racing driver like Lewis Hamilton, technical data will provide knowledge of performance.

Fabio Capello providing knowledge of performance as England manager.

KNOWLEDGE OF RESULTS (KR)

Knowledge of results (KR) tells you the outcome of your actions.

◎ You obtain KR when you watch the football fly into the net, or see how far you've thrown the javelin.
◎ The announcement of the score, or a cheer from your supporters, also provides KR.
◎ You can sometimes get KR from proprioception. At the end of a somersault on the trampoline, you can tell if you've landed correctly.

Both KP and KR will help you improve your performance. For example KR tells you that you've landed badly from a somersault. But you don't know the reason. Your coach can give you KP and suggest what to do next time.

THE IMPORTANCE OF FEEDBACK

Now that you have seen what feedback is and how the information processing system works, you will begin to realise the importance of feedback. Whether you are working on your own or with a coach the feedback you receive can help you to evaluate your performance, analyse it and plan for improvement. The more skilled you are the more use you will be able to make of the feedback, as you will understand it better.

The feedback given or received can tell you what you have done, what needs to change and even how you can make those changes so it is a new input.

QUESTIONS

1 What is **feedback**? Give three examples.
2 Name four types of feedback in sport.
3 Give three examples of ways to obtain KP.
4 KR alone will not help you improve much. Explain why.
5 Imagine you are learning a new and difficult skill. Give three reasons why feedback will help you.

6 What is meant by **intrinsic** feedback? Give an example.
7 What is meant by **extrinsic** feedback? Give an example.

Discussion work

8 How do you think the feedback a novice needs will differ from that given to a skilful performer?

9.5   LEARNING, REFINING AND ADAPTING SKILLS

• • • • In this unit you will learn how to learn and adapt skills.

Whether you are learning a new skill from scratch or you are changing a previously learned skill, the basic principles of how this is done are the same.

COPYING

One way that we learn skills is to copy someone else. Teachers often use demonstrations in PE lessons so that you can see what has to be done and try and copy it. Four things are important here:

◎ Pay *attention*. You cannot copy someone if you are not watching.
◎ *Remember* what you have seen or you won't know what to do.
◎ You must have the ability to copy what you have seen. You cannot perform the splits if you do not have the flexibility to do it yourself.
◎ You must want to learn. Without **motivation** it won't happen.

TRIAL AND ERROR

We can often learn by trial and error. We try something and if it works we do it again, if it doesn't we change it and try again. This is usually how we learn if we are teaching ourselves but coaches and teachers can help. If you are to learn skills correctly by trial and error, your coach or teacher must give appropriate feedback when you perform. If they see you do a correct move, they should praise you and point out what you have done correctly so that you learn to do it again. Alternatively, they may point out mistakes so that you do not repeat them.

ROLE MODELS

We can learn skills (and often behaviours) from role models. These are important people in our lives like a good friend, parent, teacher, coach or any other person we admire. A young footballer might have Wayne Rooney as a role model and so he looks up to him and tries to copy skills he sees him use. The best role models for learning skills from are:

◎ similar in age and ability to ourselves
◎ skilful performers
◎ someone we can identify with.

REFINING AND ADAPTING LEARNED SKILLS

Once a skill is learned it is very difficult to change it. This is a problem if we have learned a skill incorrectly. We must go back to the beginning and try to relearn the skill but without the error. This takes a lot of time, patience and practice and even then we may not be successful.

These students seem to be paying attention so they may well learn from this demonstration.

QUESTIONS

1 a When learning by copying someone else, what four factors are important? **b** Why is this so?

2 How do we learn by trial and error?

Discussion work

3 Why is it difficult to change an error once you have learned it?

9.6 TECHNOLOGICAL DEVELOPMENTS

• • • In this unit you will learn how technology is impacting on sport and how some sports are changing their laws because of it.

MATERIALS AND EQUIPMENT

In all sports, scientists and technologists are looking to improve equipment. New materials and designs can sometimes make the difference which means one performer beats another. For example, rugby shirts that help players keep hold of the ball or footballs that are easier to swerve. It is down to the sport's governing body to decide whether anything new will be allowed. If they are happy with it, top performers use it and performances improve. The governing bodies may decide the equipment is not allowed as it gives an unfair advantage or requires less skill from the athlete.

Tecnological developments have allowed Oscar Pistorius to become a top-level athlete.

TECHNOLOGY AND THE RULES

Governing bodies are changing and adapting their rules because of technology. Some of these changes are helping officials make decisions. In Rugby Union, for example, at the referee's request, a **video official** will replay the action to decide if a try has been scored. A video official is also used in other sports such as cricket. Video is also often used after games to review discipline issues.

For many years tennis has used 'Cyclops' technology to assist the officials with line calls. In more recent years the more advanced 'Hawk-Eye' technology has advanced matters, giving players in tennis and cricket the opportunity to challenge the official's decision. Other sports are trialling this so we may see it even more.

TECHNOLOGY AND TRAINING

All sports are using technology to help improve performance. Video, high-speed recording and strobe technology allows them and their coaches to scrutinise technique and make changes. ICT is also used to analyse every move. The English Cricket Board is using Hawk-Eye as a coaching aid in their high performance coaching centres. From technique adjustments to highly specialised training plans and diets, technology can play a part in it all.

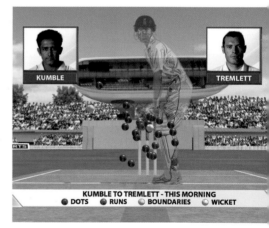

This Hawk-Eye map shows how technology can assist analysis of performance.

TECHNOLOGY AND PARTICIPATION

Technology has helped everyone. New equipment and improvements in facilities and safety factors have made some sports more accessible to everyone. Computer technology allows people to enjoy interactive games on DVD and on games consoles such as Nintendo's Wii. More people can now enjoy the thrills of skydiving and bungee jumping as technology has made them safer.

QUESTIONS

1 Name three technologies that have helped match officials make decisions during games.

2 Sometimes a governing body may ban technological advances. Why?

Discussion work

3 Do you think it is right that technology allows disabled athletes to compete alongside able-bodied athletes? Make a list of the positive and negative points.

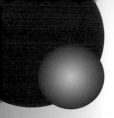

QUESTIONS ON CHAPTER 9

1 Elite performers show a great deal of skill in their sport. Using one of your sports as an example, describe the differences between a skilled and unskilled performance.

2 Skilful movement is efficient, pre-determined, co-ordinated, fluent and aesthetic. Using a skill in your sport, explain what these terms mean.

3 Many sports fall between closed and open on a continuum, like this:

closed ————————————————————— open
archery   potholing

a What is a *continuum*?

b Draw a continuum and mark these sports on it: swimming, rugby, badminton, gymnastics, canoeing

c Draw a continuum and mark these skills on it:
- a free throw in basketball
- the front crawl
- tacking (windsurfing)
- shooting at goal (football)

4 Think of your chosen practical activities.

a Describe two skills from each activity.

b Put these skills on the open and closed continuum.

c Try to say why you have put them there.

5 Draw a diagram of the information processing system, and label the parts.

6 In processing information, what is meant by:

a input?

b decision making?

c output?

d feedback?

e selective attention?

Give one example of each.

7 Most sports are made up of the **fundamental motor skills** of running, throwing, catching, kicking, jumping and hitting. Identify the fundamental motor skills used in:

a long jump   b batting in cricket

c goalkeeping in football   d your sport.

8 a What is ability?

b Think of these skills:
- mountain walking   • throwing the discus
- saving a penalty   • the splits

Name two abilities needed to perform these skills well and, in each case, say why they are important.

9 When teaching the front crawl to a friend which kind(s) of guidance would you use? Explain why your task is likely to be more difficult and less successful if you rely on:

a visual guidance only

b verbal guidance only

c manual guidance only.

10 Explain why it is better to break some skills down into parts to learn them.

a Give one example of a skill from your sport which could be learned in parts.

b Which of these skills would not be suitable to learn in parts? See if you can explain why.
- running
- the backhand in tennis
- the breast stroke
- bouncing a ball
- a somersault
- throwing a javelin

c Give one disadvantage of learning a skill in parts. How would you overcome this disadvantage?

11 Think of your chosen practical activities and list 5 skills from each one. For each skill, say whether you think fixed or variable practice is best. Now try to say why you think this is the case.

12 For which level of performer might visual guidance be most suitable?

13 When might mechanical/manual guidance best be used?

14 Explain the difference between intrinsic and extrinsic feedback. It will often depend on whether you are a novice or a skilled performer as to how much use you can make of these types of feedback. Why is this?

15 You are practising the lay-up in basketball, where you dribble in and jump to shoot the ball off the backboard and into the basket.

a How would you obtain KR?

b How would you obtain KP?

c Why do you need KP as well as KR?

16 Whether we are learning skills or behaviours, role models are important to us.

a What is a role model?

b What makes someone a good role model to learn skills from?

17 With reference to at least one of your chosen activities, list

a Three ways in which technology has improved equipment.

b Three other ways in which technology has improved performance.

18 Technology has changed the way we live our lives. How has it affected sport?

APPLIED QUESTIONS

A19 Omar is 18. He has played county level basketball for two years and has trials again soon. He has a technique error in his lay-up shot. You are his coach. How would you try to improve his technique? Refer to:

a The types of guidance you would use.

b The types of practice you would use.

c What technology you could use.

THINGS TO DO

Investigating selective attention

Think of a new skill that will be easy to teach. Divide your class into three even ability groups and teach them the task under different conditions.

GROUP 1: Make sure there are no distractions. Give the learners simple instructions and do not confuse them with any other information.

GROUP 2: Have a group of people observe them as they learn. They can try to put them off by creating a distraction.

GROUP 3: Make sure there are no distractions but try to confuse the learner by making the instructions complicated or adding irrelevant information.

At the end of the experiment ask the learners how they felt when they were learning the skill. Which group(s) found it easier to learn?

Investigating feedback

The class should divide into three groups. Each group has the same task: to draw ten 5-cm lines while blindfolded.

Group A will receive no feedback, group B will receive knowledge of results (KR) only, and group C will receive knowledge of performance (KP). Those in group A can work alone. Those in B and C will work in pairs. One person in each pair measures the lines and provides the feedback.

When you measure a line write the measurement beside it, to help you compare the results.

Group A: put on the blindfold and draw the ten lines. Now measure them to see how you did.

Group B: after each attempt, the person providing feedback measures the line and calls out 'Yes' or 'No'. He or she says nothing more.

Group C: after each attempt the person providing feedback describes how close the attempt was to success, and gives a little encouragement. For example, 'Good, just half a centimetre short'.

Compare the results for the three groups. Which group gave the best performance? What does that teach you about feedback?

Investigating guidance

For this experiment we will not use manual guidance, as some people do not like to be touched.

Think of a new skill that can easily be taught to your class and think of a way to test/measure people's performance in it. Divide the class into three even-ability groups and get one person from each group to volunteer to be the teacher.

GROUP 1 will be taught the skill using visual guidance only. The teacher will only show the group what to do. He or she cannot speak to the group at all.

GROUP 2 will be taught the skill using verbal guidance only. The teacher cannot use any kind of demonstration or other visual guidance.

GROUP 3 will be taught the skill using a combination of both types of guidance.

At the end of the experiment, test each group's performance in the skill.
1   Which group performed the skill best in the test?
2   Which group seemed to learn fastest?
3   Why do you think this was the case?
4   What did you learn about guidance by doing this experiment?

Investigating practice

Think of a new skill that can be easily broken down into parts. Divide your class into two even-ability groups and get two volunteers who will teach the skill to each group.

GROUP 1 will be taught the skill in parts. They will then put the parts together and perform the whole skill.

GROUP 2 will be taught the skill as a whole. The teacher can refer to the parts but every time the group practise the skill, they must practise the whole skill.

1   Which group seemed to learn the skill fastest?
2   Why do you think that this was the case?
3   Do you think it would be the same if we used a skill that was not easily broken down into parts?

Think of your own experiment to investigate fixed/variable practice.

Have a look at the Hawk-Eye Innovations website (www.hawkeyeinnovations.co.uk) to learn more about how this technology is being used in sport.

10.1 MOTIVATION AND GOAL SETTING

•••• In this unit you will learn about the psychological factors that make you put effort into your sport, and how you can stay motivated.

MOTIVATION

Whether you are a participant, leader or official, motivation is the driving force that makes you do what you do, and determines how much effort you put in. The more motivated you are about something the harder you will work at it, and the more likely you are to succeed. Your motivation may be *intrinsic* or *extrinsic* or a mixture of the two.

Intrinsic motivation means you do something because you get satisfaction from it. The drive comes from the activity itself. (Intrinsic means built in.) If you play a sport because you enjoy it and feel proud of your skill at it, you are intrinsically motivated.

Extrinsic motivation means you do something in order to earn money from it, or win a prize, or please another person. It is called extrinsic because it comes from outside.

Extrinsic motivators such as trophies and medals are used a great deal to encourage athletes. The Ryder Cup for golf and the FA Cup for football are examples. Money is an important motivator in some sports. The winner of the singles at Wimbledon gets a cheque for around £800 000! There are many award schemes to attract young people to sport, set up by companies and sports bodies. Extrinsic motivators are useful. But they don't always work.
◎ Not everyone feels rewards are important. (Do you?)
◎ If a reward is too difficult to obtain, or too easy, it may put you off.
◎ Competition for prizes may put you under too much pressure.
◎ A reward may lower your motivation: you feel 'bought'.
◎ Athletes may lose interest in their sport if they fail to get a prize.

But if you are intrinsically motivated, you will stick with your sport regardless of rewards. So coaches must ensure that their athletes enjoy the sport. Then when the rewards stop, the athlete doesn't.

MOTIVATION AND GOALS

One good way to stay motivated is to have a goal to work towards. For example your goal could be to perform the forward roll with your legs fully stretched, at your next attempt.
◎ A goal motivates you to work hard so it optimises your performance.
◎ It helps you to prepare mentally for a performance, since you know exactly what you are aiming for.
◎ It is like a signpost in your training, giving you direction.
◎ It also gives you something to check your progress against.
◎ Having a goal makes you feel less anxious, and more in control.
◎ Meeting your goal increases your confidence.

Extrinsic motivators have a high profile in athletics.

WHAT MAKES A GOOD GOAL?

Think SMART!

S **is for specific**. A goal such as 'I must run faster' is too vague. 'I must run 30 metres in under 4 seconds at my next attempt' is much more specific. It gives you something definite to focus on.

M is for measurable. '30 metres in under 4 seconds' is a measurable goal. You can check if you've been successful and so gauge your progress.

A is for agreed. You and your coach should discuss and agree about your goals. It gives you ownership of the goals so you value them. If you're not happy with them, they won't motivate you.

R is for realistic. A realistic goal is one which is *achievable*. '30 metres in 2 seconds' is unrealistic. If a goal is too difficult it will put you off. But it must also be challenging; if it's too easy you'll get bored. It also helps if the goal is **recorded**.

T is for time-phased. Your goals should be planned in advance to give you a time-scale. A *short-term* goal for a tennis beginner could be 'serve the ball over the net 3 times this training session'. A *long-term* goal could be 'get 80% of my first serves in by the end of the season'.

Have a specific goal in mind every time you practise your sport. You'll find it makes a lot of difference.

Goals can also be *performance* goals or *outcome* goals. Performance goals are concerned with how well you do compared with previous performances. They help you aim for your end result. Outcome goals are concerned with the end result, which is often to win! Unfortunately this may mean win at all costs.

MOTIVATION, AROUSAL AND MENTAL PREPARATION

Motivation is linked with arousal. Arousal is a state of readiness or alertness. All athletes need to be aroused if they are to perform at their best but this is an individual thing. Whereas some athletes need to increase their arousal, others need to control it. Athletes can learn to control their arousal levels by using several techniques:

◎ **Relaxation.** Techniques include slow deep breathing and relaxing different muscles in turn.

◎ **Mental rehearsal.** This is where you imagine yourself performing your event. You 'see' yourself performing well and staying calm and confident.

◎ **Focusing.** You concentrate completely on the activity you are about to perform. You do not allow any distractions to affect your concentration.

QUESTIONS

1 What is motivation?

2 Explain the difference between **intrinsic** and **extrinsic** motivation.

3 Give three examples of extrinsic motivators.

4 Name one extrinsic motivator connected with your sport.

5 Give four reasons why goals help an athlete.

6 What is the difference between short-term and long-term goals? Give an example of each

7 What motivates you to play your sport? There may be several different factors.

8 What motivates coaches and officials? Do you think this is different from the motivation for performers?

Discussion work

9 Plan some sports goals for yourself for the next six months. Discuss them with your teacher or coach.

10.2   PSYCHOLOGICAL RISK FACTORS

●●●● In this unit you will learn about the psychological factors concerned with fatigue and stress.

Taking part in physical activity involves risk to the body. Obviously this can be physical, as you learned in unit 4.7, but damage can also be psychological and this is often harder to mend.

WHAT ARE STRESS AND FATIGUE?

Stress is what you feel when you cannot cope with the demands being put upon you. The amount of stress you feel varies from day to day and it is also different for different people. Fatigue is the weariness you feel when you have done too much; again this can be physical or psychological.

THE CAUSES AND EFFECTS OF STRESS AND FATIGUE

There are many factors that impact on stress and it is important that you and your coach know what is likely to affect you and how you can control it.

◎ **Personality/emotions**. We are all different. Some of us are shy or quiet whilst others are lively and outgoing. Our personality and emotions often determine our behaviour and even our choice of activity. If we are put into a situation we are uncomfortable with, stress can occur. For example, if you are the quiet type and prefer to be on your own, you may experience stress if you are asked to lead an activity or join a group training session. You are out of your comfort zone.

◎ **Tension/anxiety**. Sport can produce a lot of anxiety. You may get anxious before a competition or if your training isn't going well. Good mental preparation and goal setting will hopefully prevent this. See unit 10.1.

◎ **Aggression**. When some people get stressed they may become aggressive. If you can channel your aggression into your sport, this could be a good thing. However, some people let their aggression get the better of them and they may react badly. They could become violent or abusive and fair play might suffer.

◎ **Motivation/arousal**. This can determine how well you perform. A lack of motivation or arousal means you can become bored and performance suffers but over-arousal can also affect how well you do! It is important that you prepare yourself mentally to perform at your best and avoid the stress of doing badly. See unit 10.1

◎ **Feedback/criticism**. We all react differently to criticism. If things aren't going well or we receive too much negative feedback from our performance or coach, we are likely to get stressed. Your coach really should know this and take steps to make sure it doesn't happen.

Staying calm and controlling your nerves can help to reduce stress.

QUESTIONS

1 What is stress?

2 What is fatigue?

3 How can they affect your performance?

Discussion work

4 Do you think psychological damage is harder to mend than physical injury? Explain your answer.

10.3 LEADERSHIP

In this unit you will learn about leadership and its importance in sport.

Leadership is what you do to influence other people and guide them towards meeting their goals. In sport the leader could be a team captain, coach, manager or official, so they are very important people. The way they do their job can affect your performance.

STYLES OF LEADERSHIP

There are different styles of leadership. The style you adopt is dependent on your personality, the people you are leading and the job you have to do.

◎ **Autocratic**. This is sometimes known as the authoritarian style. With this style the leader makes most if not all of the decisions. The leader has the job to be done uppermost in their mind and may not think too much about other people's thoughts and feelings.

◎ **Democratic**. With this style the leader is more concerned with people than with the job to be done. The leader shares decisions with the team and asks their opinions.

◎ **Laissez-faire**. With this style, the leader lets the team make the decisions. They choose what they are going to do and get very little input from the leader.

A good leader varies the style they use depending on the situation. If a decision is needed quickly, the autocratic style is often best whereas if time allows, a more democratic approach can be used. Sometimes it is better to be democratic in training and autocratic in a competition.

WHAT MAKES LEADERSHIP SUCCESSFUL?

Leadership is most successful when the style of leadership used is also the one that is needed. In other words, if the leader is being autocratic and that's what the team want and the job to be done requires it, then a successful result is likely to be achieved. If any one of those things is missing then the result might not be successful.

Leadership style	Good points	Disadvantages
Autocratic	Decisions can be made quickly Good with large teams Task gets done	Task is more important than the people Might not bring out the best in the team
Democratic	Less formal approach Individuals more likely to develop	Decision making takes time Large teams means people might not agree
Laissez-faire	Encourages others to use their initiative	May result in poor decision making May be a lack of focus Task may not get done

Qualities of good leadership
- able to make effective decisions
- good role model
- able to relate to others
- good at communication
- enthusiastic
- able to motivate
- determined and ambitious.

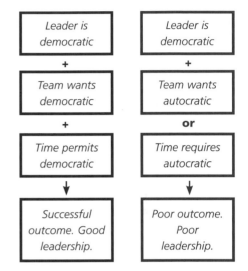

Leader is democratic	Leader is democratic
+	**+**
Team wants democratic	Team wants autocratic
+	**or**
Time permits democratic	Time requires autocratic
↓	↓
Successful outcome. Good leadership.	Poor outcome. Poor leadership.

Dave Brailsford, leader of the British Cycling team in Beijing, showed excellent leadership as the team won 14 medals, 8 of them gold.

QUESTIONS

1 What is meant by the term leadership?

2 Name the three styles of leadership?

3 Give four qualities of a good leader.

Discussion work

4 You will have acted as a leader in your sport at some time. What style of leadership do you think you adopted?

QUESTIONS ON CHAPTER 10

1 Below are some reasons for taking part in sport. Match each item i to iv to a letter A or B.

   A extrinsic motivation

   B intrinsic motivation

      i wanting to please a parent or teacher

      ii enjoying the movements in sport

      iii wanting to win the gold medal

      iv wanting to improve your skill

2 You probably have several motives for playing your favourite sport and they may have changed over the years.

   a Write a list of all the motives you have ever used.

   b Now place them in order of importance.

   c Beside each, write down whether it is intrinsic or extrinsic.

   d Which are the more important to you, intrinsic or extrinsic?

   e Has this changed since you were younger?

3 **a** What do we mean by a goal when we talk about goal setting?

   b Here are two different goals:

      i To do my best in this event.

      ii To do two more press-ups today than I did yesterday in the same time.

   Which is the better goal? Explain why.

4 A good goal can be summed up by the word SMART.

   a What does each letter stand for?

   b Explain what each term means.

5 How can preparing mentally help you to control your emotions? How does this help to keep fair play?

6 Think about how you feel when you are stressed. How would this affect your physical performance?

7 How do you cope with the stress of competition?

8 How might the following cause stress:

   a emotions

   b anxiety

   c boredom

   d criticism.

9 With each of the above (a–d) give one way in which you might be able to overcome the stress.

10 A possible problem for athletes is aggression. Describe two negative ways in which this might be displayed.

11 How can aggression be a good thing in sport?

12 Describe the three styles of leadership.

13 A good leader should be able to vary their style of leadership. Why is this important?

APPLIED QUESTIONS

Jemma is 28. She has competed many times for England as a marathon runner. She trains full time but has missed two months of her normal training due to a stress fracture in her foot. She has now done two weeks of pain-free gentle running on a treadmill but is worried that she will not be ready for the London marathon in 3 months time. You are her coach.

A14 How would you motivate her over the next months?

A15 Set her some SMART goals for the next 3 months One long-term and several short-term.

A16 She is anxious about the forthcoming race. What possible damage might this cause to her confidence? What could you do to help her?

A17 What style of leadership would you use with her, bearing in mind she is an individual athlete?

A18 Would this style of leadership change as you got closer to the race? Why?

THINGS TO DO

Goal setting

Setting goals can help you in all areas of life, not just sport. This shows a form for recording your goals and checking how well you met them.

My goals for: _____
Goal 1: _____
Goal 2: _____
How I did _____

Try this out for different kinds of goals. For example:

a your next piece of homework. Your goals could be about the time you spend and how many mistakes you make.

b your next sports training session.

Investigating motivation

You will ask three groups of people to do standing broad jumps. Each group will need a start line marked on the floor, and someone with a tape to measure and record the jumps.

a Randomly choose three groups A, B and C, with 6 people in each group. Each person will do 3 jumps. The longest of the 3 will be recorded.

b Group A goes first. This group does the jumps in private, away from the class, and gets no feedback of any kind.

c Group B goes next. This group also works in private. But before starting the group is told that the two best performers will get a prize. Say what the prize is, e.g. a Mars bar.

d Group C goes last. The group jumps in front of the class. There is no prize, but the class is very encouraging and gives friendly and positive feedback, e.g. they can cheer.

e The average jump for each group is calculated, by adding the 6 longest jumps and dividing by 6.

f Compare the results of the three groups. What do you notice? Explain it using the idea of motivation.

Which kind of motivation worked best?

A relaxation technique

This method of relaxation is called centering.

1 Stand comfortably with your feet apart and your knees slightly bent.

2 Relax your face, neck, arm and shoulder muscles, until you feel all the tension has drained from them.

3 Still remaining relaxed, take a deep breath. Concentrate on your diaphragm. Move your chest as little as possible.

4 Now breathe out slowly and let yourself go. You will feel heavier as your muscles relax.

5 Practise this for just 1 minute a day for two weeks, in front of a mirror if possible.

Once you have learned this technique, you will be able to use it to calm down any time you feel nervous.

Visualization (mental rehearsal)

What is your next important event? It could be a sports event or an exam. Visualization will help you prepare.

1 Sit or lie down comfortably.

2 Close your eyes and breathe deeply until you feel really relaxed.

3 Now go through the event in your mind, step by step.

Imagine you are in control and performing very well. Notice how you are feeling. Notice the different problems that arise and how well you deal with them.

Do this several times a day before the event. Think of all the problems that might arise and how you deal with each of them.

The technique is also useful when you are learning a new skill. You go through it lots of times in your mind, step by step.

11.1 LEISURE AND THE SPORTS PARTICIPATION PYRAMID

In this unit you will learn about leisure time and why someone participates in sport – and why some people go on to succeed at a higher level.

LEISURE

Leisure is how you spend your free time, when you can do as you please. Perhaps you like to watch TV, or play computer games, or abseil down a cliff face. What you choose to do will depend on your culture and upbringing, your social class, and the facilities available. For example most homes have a TV, but you need to be rich or have rich friends to play polo.

THE GROWTH IN LEISURE

As a society, we have more and more time for leisure. (You may not have noticed!) There are several reasons for this:

◎ Improvements in technology mean that machines are taking over more of our work. This leaves more people unemployed or in part-time work, or forced to take early retirement.
◎ Labour-saving devices also cut the time for household chores.
◎ Improvements in health care and the standard of living mean we are living longer. The number of active retired people is increasing.
◎ Some people choose to work less, to reduce the stress in their lives. Some choose to **job-share** with another person.

This is a challenge to the government which must provide facilities for leisure: parks, playing fields, swimming pools and so on. It is also a challenge to the leisure industry which provides holidays, theme parks, bowling alleys, ice rinks, cinemas, theatres, rock concerts and fitness centres, with the aim of making a profit.

WHY PARTICIPATE IN PHYSICAL ACTIVITIES?

There are lots of good reasons for taking up a physical activity and many benefits from doing so. We can classify these into three groups: social, physical and mental.

Social. Sport is fun and it gives you the opportunity to spend time with your friends, make new friends, and work together co-operatively.

Mental. Sport can provide you with a challenge and an opportunity for healthy competition. It can give you the chance to work and succeed at a higher level which will increase your self-esteem and confidence. It can also help to relieve stress.

Physical. You might take up jogging or swimming for health reasons. As you learned on pages 8–11, taking part in a physical activity can help you improve your body shape and fitness levels. You look and feel better and will probably live longer. You may want to improve your performance level in your chosen activity. For some people physical activity is not a leisure activity – it's their job!

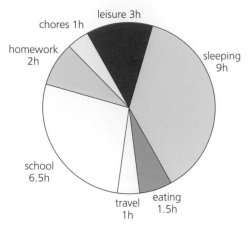

How the day is spent.

They may have decided to follow a career in sport as their **vocation**. This means that it's their full-time or part-time job. Professional and semi-professional sports people get paid to participate in their sport. But it's not just sports people who have a vocation in sport. You may choose to become a coach, PE teacher, trainer, or physiotherapist, or to go into sports management.

THE SPORTS PARTICIPATION PYRAMID

Let's take athletics as an example:

◎ The FOUNDATION stage – Nearly everyone has taken part in an athletics activity at the very basic level. You have probably raced your friends in the park and taken part in a PE lesson at school. The foundation stage is the base and nearly the entire population fits into this category.

◎ The PARTICIPATION stage – Some people may wish to take things further. You may decide to go to an after-school or lunchtime club and get more coaching and the opportunity to compete against other schools. You have chosen to pursue athletics further and not everyone will do this.

◎ The PERFORMANCE stage – At this stage people are becoming more skilled at athletics. You may have been selected to compete at County or Regional level. If you have left school, participating in athletics may take more effort on your part. You may have joined an athletics club to get specialist coaching and compete at adult level. You may compete at national level against some of the best athletes in the country.

◎ The ELITE stage – The top of the pyramid is where we find the very best athletes. Not only are you now competing at national and international level, but you may now be making money from athletics. People pay to see you perform and you may get appearance money and sponsorship deals. You could have your own coach and train full-time.

You can see that the number of people moving up to the next stage gets fewer each time, but it doesn't happen by accident. It takes a lot of determination and hard work and the further up you go, the more skill is needed. But hard work and skill aren't the only factors at play. On pages 14–17 you learned about the physical factors that help to determine how far up the pyramid someone might go. Over the next few pages you will learn about a lot of other factors that affect someone's participation in sport at every stage of the pyramid.

A pyramid shows that from a large base of people taking part, some go on to perform at higher levels, whilst only a few reach the top.

QUESTIONS

1 What is leisure?

2 Why do we have an increasing amount of leisure time?

3 Reasons why people participate in sport are classified into 3 groups. What are they? Describe what they mean?

4 How can sport become a vocation for some people?

5 Explain the sports participation pyramid using a team sport.

Discussion work

6 How do you spend your day?

11.2 FACTORS AFFECTING PARTICIPATION

In this unit you will learn about the factors that affect why people participate and in what activity. You will learn that each factor has positive and negative effects.

In the last unit we have seen why people take part in an activity but what encourages people to choose a particular activity? What makes one activity more popular than another? There are many factors at work.

PEER GROUP

Your peers are the people you mix with who have similar interests and backgrounds and are roughly your age. Your peer group tends to have a big influence on the way you behave and the things that you do. This is not always expressed in words. If you wear the 'wrong' clothes or do the 'wrong' things you can quickly feel left out.

If your friends enjoy PE at school then it is likely that they will encourage you to enjoy it too. When you go to a sports club or extra-curricular activity and find lots of your peer group there as well, that will encourage you to keep going. Sadly, peer group pressure can have the opposite effect if you find that they do not 'approve' of the activity you have chosen. It may be that you would rather spend time socialising with your peers than training for your sport. Some people give up sports, even though they enjoy them, because of the effect of their peers.

FAMILY

When you are very young, your family has more influence on you than your peers. We therefore pick up many of our habits and values from home. If your family enjoys sport and gives you the opportunity to participate, then it is likely that you will. Again, the opposite is also true which means that if your family has a negative attitude to sport the chances are that will be passed onto you.

A positive attitude from your family is not always enough to get you participating in a particular activity. Most young people depend upon parents and family for financial help and help with travel to sports events and training. If you are lucky then your family can provide this support but obviously not all families can afford it.

GENDER

There is a mistaken belief held by some people that sport is a man's world. There certainly seem to be fewer barriers put up to prevent men from participating in physical activity. Far more men participate in physical activities than women. But why is this? Some of the reasons are historical:

◎ The traditional roles of wife and mother have left little time or energy for sport.
◎ Not many leisure centres used to offer crèche facilities.
◎ Women who didn't have their own job often didn't have the money to spend on physical recreation.

Support from family and friends is important.

In 2007 from over 30 000 football referees in England, only 14 women had progressed beyond county level.

◎ There has been a shortage of role models.
◎ Little media coverage has been given to women's sports in the past.
◎ Women's sports have found it harder to gain sponsorship.

Participation by women is increasing as more emphasis is placed on exercise for good health. Increased provision for women such as crèche facilities at leisure centres for women with young children, woman-only activities and promotion to women by bodies such as the Sports Councils have all helped to make the number of female participants go up.

There are far more women being seen to be successful in sport and destroying some of the old myths. Cyclist Victoria Pendleton and tennis star Ana Ivanovic are living proof that it is possible to be a successful athlete and still remain 'feminine'.

We are also seeing more women take up other roles in sport. There are an increasing number of women becoming managers, coaches and officials, even in men's sports, and there are far more women presenting sport on TV.

Race

People from minority ethnic groups can be discriminated against when it comes to physical activities. Many people have the mistaken belief that they are physiologically different because they are a different colour, and this means they will be good at some activities and not others. For example, some people believe that all black people are fast runners and they cannot swim very well. This belief could be the reason why we see so many black runners and few black swimmers.

Socio-economics

The activity you participate in may be determined to a large extent by what you can afford. Activities like sailing, golf and riding can be very expensive and so many people from lower socio-economic groups are excluded from them. There are also many activities that cost very little. A kick-around in the park with a group of friends, for example, and sport at school are mostly free. Unemployed people are in a difficult situation: plenty of time to fill but not much money. To encourage them, sports facilities often charge less, especially at quiet times of the day.

In 2004, Martiza Correia became the first black swimmer to be selected for the US Olympic team.

QUESTIONS

1 Give three positive ways in which participation in sport may be affected by your:
   a peer group, **b** family, **c** race, **d** socio-economic group.

2 Give three negative ways in which participation in sport may be affected by your:
   a peer group, **b** family, **c** race, **d** socio-economic group.

Discussion work

3 How have these factors affected your participation in sport?

11.3   FURTHER FACTORS AFFECTING PARTICIPATION

• • • • • In this unit you will learn about some more reasons why people participate in sport and why some may choose not to participate.

It's important for all age groups to have access to an activity they enjoy. Bowls has always been popular among older people.

AGE

Young people are encouraged to participate at school and have plenty of free time to take up a sport. It also depends on the activity. To be a good gymnast you need to be young and flexible. Today, however, with computer technology not all youngsters want to spend their free time playing sport and not all sports are open to very young people, e.g. to compete in a full power-lifting competition, you have to be 14. People tend to take part less in physical recreation as they get older as they often have more responsibilities and less free time to spend on sport. Stereotyping can mean that older people are discouraged from being physically active. Some older people stereotype themselves and believe that they are too old to take part in physical activity. However, there are many sports that you can enjoy into your old age. All you need is the motivation to do it, the right facilities and no barriers to prevent you.

DISABILITY

A disability may restrict your activities and other people's prejudice can be a barrier to your participation. But disabled sport has received a much higher profile since the Paralympic Games in Sydney, and the efforts of disabled athletes like Tanni Grey-Thompson have provided disabled people with excellent role models. Many sports have changed their rules to suit the needs of disabled people and have set up coaching and competitions for them. Facilities must now include ramps and lifts and special changing rooms so that disabled people can have full access.

Disabled sport now has a much higher profile than in the past.

ACCESS

If there is a sports facility near to where you live, and there is a good road system and public transport in place, then getting there is made easy. However, many people do not live within easy reach of sports facilities, and the public transport system is poor, so participation is made more difficult.

POPULARITY, PROMOTION AND ROLE MODELS

Participation in many sports varies. Because of media coverage during Wimbledon fortnight, tennis courts across the country are heavily used, as seeing role models perform on TV encourages people to play the sport themselves. Not all sports attract media attention, however, and not all media attention is positive (see pages 165–166). Some activities are promoted by the governing body or even the government. In 2008 the government gave local authorities new funding to try and encourage the under 16s and over 60s to go swimming.

ENVIRONMENT AND CLIMATE

Participation in some activities also depends upon the environment and climate. It is very hard to become a top skier if you live in a hot country and, if you want to practise mountaineering and you live in Holland, you have got to travel. So it is not hard to understand why countries like Switzerland and Canada produce very good skiers. Britain is traditionally good at sailing because it is an island and surrounded by water.

TRADITION AND CULTURE

Tradition and culture also affect participation. For example, some cultures disapprove of women taking part in physical recreation in public or in mixed company. This is one reason why many sports centres operate 'women only' sessions. Most sports have had a tradition of being male only. Women have had to work hard to be allowed to participate.

EDUCATION

Your education has a big effect on your attitude to sport and physical recreation. If your school is keen on sport you will be encouraged to participate and if you enjoy it, you are likely to continue after you leave. The opposite is also true, however, for those who dislike PE. It is known that there is a drop in participation at the age of 16 when youngsters leave school. This is known as the post-school gap and is perhaps caused by the desire to leave all school-based activities behind you when you leave. Thankfully, many young people then see the benefits of physical activity and return to it a little later in their life.

CONFIDENCE AND SELF-ESTEEM

As you saw in unit 1.2, taking part in sport can boost your self-confidence and help to give you a positive image of yourself. Unfortunately for some people the opposite can also be true. If you have had a bad experience with sport or PE you may not wish to participate again. Some people feel very self-conscious about taking part in a public place as they feel everyone is watching them. Others have a low opinion of their own ability. Some facilities hold special sessions to try and encourage people who feel this way and with developments in technology there are more activities you can do in your own front room!

HEALTH

There can be no doubt that physical activity is good for your health (even if we may suffer from the odd injury!). But for some people health reasons restrict or even prevent them from taking part. An illness, serious injury or a debilitating condition such as arthritis may have a big impact on your desire and ability to be active.

British Olympic sailors performed particularly well in Sydney 2000.

QUESTIONS

1 Give two reasons why people may stop participating in sport as they get older.

2 Name two sports that are traditionally popular in the UK.

3 We can categorise the key influences that impact on people's participation into four main areas: resources, people, image of the activity and cultural factors. Give two examples under each heading and explain how they are an influence.

Discussion work

4 What factors have affected you in your participation of sport and/or physical activity?

11.4   PROVISION

• • • • In this unit you will learn about the provision of facilities which enable an active, healthy lifestyle.

Some facilities for sport and recreation are built. Examples are tennis courts, swimming pools, running tracks, gyms, and reservoirs used as water sports centres.

Others are natural: lakes, rivers, the sea, hills, forests and mountains. But even these must be planned and looked after. They may need car parks, rubbish bins, marked footpaths, toilets and information centres. They may need areas marked out for different use. For example fishing and water skiing don't go together. Why?

These people are enjoying an active lifestyle thanks to the provision of local facilities.

WHO PROVIDES FACILITIES?

Local authorities. Your local council probably owns most of the local sports facilities: playing fields, tennis courts, pitch and putt, swimming pools and so on. Many local authorities employ Sports Development Officers. Their job is to promote sport within their area by creating links between schools and local clubs. Some officers cover one sport over a large area, such as a whole county. Others cater for many sports in a smaller area such as a town or district. The local education authority owns most schools and their facilities. Some school facilities are dual purpose – local people also use them in the evenings. This way they get maximum use, and the links between the school and community are strengthened.

Private enterprise. Many facilities are set up and run by businesses in order to make profit. For example, private gyms and golf clubs. Some are attached to hotels but also open to the locals. Some are very exclusive and membership may cost thousands of pounds a year. Others include theme parks such as Alton Towers and holiday facilities such as Center Parcs.

Voluntary organisations. These are bodies set up to meet a need rather than make a profit. There are lots of them, including local sports clubs, youth clubs, churches and charities. Between them they provide a wide variety of activities which is important when trying to encourage an active lifestyle. The wider the choice, the more likely a high number of people will participate. You may be able to choose from a gymnastics club at your local church hall or a leisurely bike ride at a track through your local woods, for example.

National authorities. The government has set up sports councils such as UK Sport and Sport England. Each individual sport has a governing body. Between them they promote sport participation and assist top-class athletes, providing facilities and opportunities for all. You can learn more about this in unit 12.1.

THE LOCATION OF FACILITIES

Where are facilities located? It depends on several factors:

◎ **Expected use and demand.** There is no point building a leisure centre miles from anywhere, with no one to use it. You will lose money on the venture. Most facilities are built in or near towns and cities where the demand is high.

◎ **The natural environment.** Canoeing and sailing clubs need to be beside water. Facilities for climbers need to be close to the mountains.

◎ **Cost.** Land is more expensive in some areas than others. A developer may be forced to choose a cheaper area. Even in a cheaper area, a local council may be unable to afford new facilities. But there are ways round this. It could qualify for a grant from the government or the EU, or for a Lottery Sports Fund award.

◎ **Access.** A facility must be easy to get to, especially if it's out of town. That means close to good roads and within reach of public transport.

◎ **Acceptability.** Not all facilities are welcomed by everyone. Every facility needs planning permission from the local authority. Local people get a chance to express their views. They may object to a facility that will 'spoil' a beauty spot, or bring more noise and traffic to the area.

MEETING THE USERS' NEEDS

If we are to provide opportunities for all to participate it is important to meet the users' needs. Some providers offer subsidies to make facilities affordable for everyone. **Target groups** of people such as women, the over 50s, those with disabilities and ethnic minorities are encouraged by specific group sessions just for them. Minority sports promote themselves by advertising and offering taster courses.

Some facilities are fairly evenly spread. Others aren't. Where's your nearest water-skiing facility?

QUESTIONS

1 Find two local examples of a recreational facility: **a** which is owned by the local council **b** which is privately owned **c** which is provided by a voluntary organization.

2 A local sports centre may need to cater for several different groups of users. List as many as you can.

3 How might a swimming pool cater for many different user groups.

Discussion work

4 Visit your local council website to find a list of activities on offer. Who is providing each activity? Categorise them into **a** local authority, **b** private enterprise, **c** voluntary organisations and **d** national authorities.

11.5   PE IN SCHOOL

In this unit you will learn about the role of your school curriculum in promoting a healthy lifestyle.

The government has placed great importance on PE in school and this doesn't just mean your PE lessons! There are other lessons you have at school that contribute.

WHY IS PE IN SCHOOL IMPORTANT?

◎ It helps you learn about yourself and your abilities.
◎ It helps to develop teamwork and a sense of fair play.
◎ It helps you develop a fit and healthy body.
◎ It helps you develop self-confidence.
◎ It gives you the chance to enjoy yourself.
◎ If you get into the habit of regular exercise at school, you are more likely to adopt a healthy lifestyle later.
◎ It might even lead to a career for you.

PE IN THE NATIONAL CURRICULUM

From the beginning of Key Stage 1 to the end of Key Stage 4, everyone must take PE in school as part of the National Curriculum. Your school has the responsibility of promoting participation in physical activity by offering you a variety of opportunities in a range of activities.

At primary school, dance, games and gymnastic activities start off your curriculum experience, with swimming and water safety, athletics and outdoor and adventurous activities being introduced as you get older. At secondary school these activities continue with the emphasis being on the skills required to outwit opponents, solve problems or exercise safely, for example. Throughout your school career you should be given opportunities to learn and apply skills, make decisions, evaluate and improve performance and make informed choices about following a healthy lifestyle.

QUALIFICATIONS

You can gain a number of qualifications in PE, which means that you can enjoy the subject and perhaps get a qualification that may help you find a job later. Not all schools offer this opportunity as it depends on the teachers you have and whether or not they want you to do exams and written work. Some people believe that PE should just be about practical work. Your school may also give you the opportunity to gain proficiency awards in specific sports e.g. the British Gymnastics Proficiency Awards.

ADOPTING DIFFERENT ROLES

Schools encourage students to try lots of different roles in PE lessons. This way it is hoped that everyone will find some part of PE they enjoy. If you do not like actually performing, maybe you will enjoy coaching, officiating or observing. Maybe your strength lies in organising or choreography. Roles such as captain or leader will help those who like performing to take on more responsibility as well.

You have a wide choice of qualifications you can take in PE
- Entry level PE
- Awards
  › Sports Leader UK awards
  › Progression awards in sport and leisure
- National Vocational Qualifications (NVQ)
  › Sports development and the sport and leisure industry
- GCSE
  › Expressive Arts
  › Dance
  › PE
  › PE (short course)
- A/AS level
  › Expressive Arts
  › Dance
  › PE
- BTEC
  › National Diplomas Level 2 & 3
  › National Certificates Level 2 & 3
- OCR Nationals.

THE HEALTHY SCHOOLS PROGRAMME

This is a long-term programme which aims to improve the links between health, behaviour and achievement. It is based on a whole-school approach to physical and emotional well-being and is based around four main themes:

◉ **Personal, Social and Health Education (PSHE)**. This is taught in a variety of ways. Some schools have it as a separate lesson on the timetable and include topics such as drugs education and sex and relationships education. Other schools teach it as a cross-curricular subject and hold health awareness days with activities and workshops on topics such as smoking, teenage pregnancy or personal safety.

◉ **Healthy eating**. Thanks to the efforts of TV chef Jamie Oliver, this has become high profile in British schools. The Healthy Schools programme puts emphasis on free drinking water in school as well as healthy meal options (even if you take a packed lunch!).

◉ **Physical activity**. This is not just about your PE lessons but also encourages walking/cycling to and from school, extracurricular activities and the involvement of staff, parents and carers.

◉ **Emotional health and well-being**. This helps you to recognise and understand your feelings and build your confidence and self-esteem.

THE USE OF INFORMATION AND COMMUNICATIONS TECHNOLOGY (ICT)

Schools are increasingly using ICT in all subjects and PE is no different. ICT software is sometimes used to help review and improve performance and this also helps with your development of key skills. Some schools are even using games consoles such as the Nintendo Wii to supplement their PE programme.

QUESTIONS

1 Apart from performer, what other roles might you be encouraged to adopt in PE lessons?

2 Why is **observer** not acceptable as a role in PE lessons?

3 Name four different qualifications you could gain in PE.

4 What are the four themes of the Healthy Schools Programme that contribute to the promotion of a healthy lifestyle?

5 How is ICT being used in PE lessons?

Discussion work

6 Some people think PE should not be offered as an exam subject. Do you agree with this? Why?

11.6 SPORT IN SCHOOL

In this unit you will learn about the extra-curricular opportunities in schools and the community links made.

In the previous unit you looked at the curriculum at school, in other words, what you are taught in lessons. Sport in school is concerned with the physical activities you are involved in outside lesson time: it is **extra-curricular**.

WHAT PHYSICAL ACTIVITIES CAN A SCHOOL OFFER?

It depends on:

◎ The expertise available. A school can't offer an activity if there is no-one to lead it. However, you will learn how schools are getting help with this later in this unit.

◎ The attitude of the staff. If a teacher is really keen on an activity their enjoyment for it can be passed on to you. (Unfortunately, the opposite can also be true.) Many teachers give up free time at lunchtime, after school and weekends to run sports and other extra-curricular activities. Sadly, teachers now often have less free time to give than in the past because of increased marking, assessments and preparation.

◎ The facilities available. Schools don't always have the money or space for good facilities and a lack of playing fields can be a big problem, especially in city schools. Many schools get round this by using local facilities or sharing those of another nearby school. It may be that your school organises activity courses for you where you might even spend time away from home, such as a residential outdoor activity holiday.

PE SCHOOL SPORT AND CLUB LINKS (PESSCL)

The government launched this strategy in 2002 with the aim of increasing the number of 5–16 year olds participating in sport. The long-term goal is to have all children taking part in at least four hours of sport every week by 2010. This is to be made up of two hours PE and two hours extra-curricular sport.

In Wales, the Welsh Assembly and the Sports Council for Wales have launched the **5x60 initiative** which sets the target of 90 per cent of secondary pupils receiving 60 minutes of physical activity 5 times per week by 2020.

Both of these strategies aim to achieve their targets by speaking to young people to find out what they would like to do and what barriers are preventing them from currently doing it. After the initial success of PESSCL the strategy was extended to produce a world class system for PE and sport leading up to the Olympics of 2012.

Dame Kelly Holmes is the National School Sport Champion.

As you can see from this graph the number of young people participating is increasing. So the strategies are possibly having an effect.

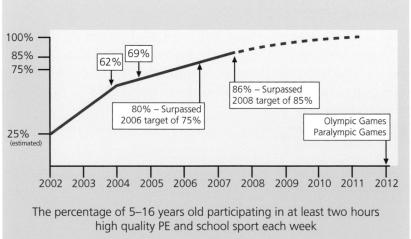

100%
85%
75%

62%   69%

80% – Surpassed
2006 target of 75%

86% – Surpassed
2008 target of 85%

Olympic Games
Paralympic Games

25%
(estimated)

2002 2003 2004 2005 2006 2007 2008 2009 2010 2011 2012

The percentage of 5–16 years old participating in at least two hours high quality PE and school sport each week

Crown Copyright 2008

HOW DOES PESSCL ACTUALLY WORK IN SCHOOLS?

The strategy centres on Specialist Sports Colleges who work with other local schools, both secondary and primary, to share expertise and facilities.

Schools work closely together to provide you with the activities you want. If your school doesn't have the facilities or the teachers to run an activity, then arrangements are made to use the facilities of another school or local club. A specialist coach may be brought in just to run an after-school club or lunchtime club. This means that a lot more activities are available and so there is likely to be more people participating. Because of the community links built with local clubs, it is hoped that you will continue with the activity after you have left school.

These youngsters are enjoying an interschool sports competition organised by their partner school.

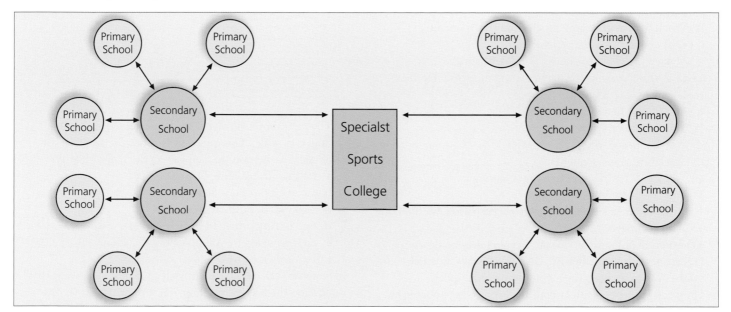

SCHOOL SPORT AND LIFELONG ACTIVITY

It is hoped that by enjoying the clubs and competitions of your extra-curricular sport, you will build positive attitudes which will make you want to continue your sport when you leave school. It may be that you become involved in increasingly complex and challenging activities and go on to be a top performer or maybe you follow a sport-related career. Some people continue their sport by becoming coaches and volunteering to coach at local clubs or by organising local events. However you take part, sport and other physical activities can give you valuable skills such as co-operation with others, competition, a physical challenge and the pleasure of simply enjoying what you do (aesthetic appreciation).

QUESTIONS

1 What is meant by the term extra-curricular activities?

2 Give two examples of extra-curricular sport.

3 What does **PESSCL** stand for?

4 Give two reasons that would encourage young people to go to extra-curricular activities.

5 How could cycling give you competition, co-operation, physical challenge and aesthetic appreciation?

Discussion work

6 How do schools promote a healthy, active lifestyle?

QUESTIONS ON CHAPTER 11

1 Is it a leisure activity? Explain why.
  a playing netball at lunchtime at school
  b eating meals at home
  c going to the cinema
  d sleeping at night
  e cycling to school
  f playing cards with your friends

2 a Make a list of all the things you do in a normal week.
  b Divide your list into essential and leisure activities.
  c Divide your leisure activities into physical and non-physical.
  d Work out roughly how much time you spend on each activity in a normal week.
  e Make a pie chart to show the information.

3 Look at these reasons for participating in sport. Are they social, mental or physical?
  a You like to be with your friends
  b You want to stay fit
  c You feel proud when you do well
  d You want to lose weight
  e You feel less stressed after participating
  f You get to meet new people

4 Name the four levels in the sports participation pyramid. Explain each level.

5 Whether or not you participate in sport may be down to the influence of your family. Give three ways in which your family may encourage you to take up a sport.

6 How can your peers affect your decision to take part in an activity?

7 The government has created target groups of people it would like to see participating more in sport. Name three.

8 Surveys over recent years have shown some interesting statistics on sports participation:
  • Women's participation is 14 per cent below that of men.
  • Black and ethnic participation is 6 per cent below the national average.
  • 38 per cent of disabled people participate as opposed to 59 per cent of non-disabled people.
  • People in the professional social class are three times more likely to participate then those in the unskilled manual group.
  a Give three reasons why women might participate less than men.
  b Why might people with more money be participating more in sport?
  c Why might people from ethnic minority groups participate less than average?
  d What can be done to encourage disabled people to participate more?

9

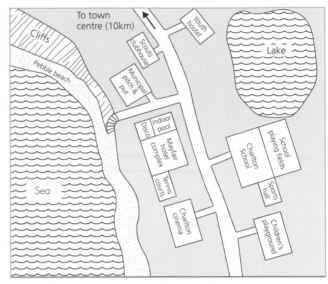

The map above shows part of a coastal town. It is not drawn to scale. This question is about the facilities for physical recreation that appear on the map. Identify:
  a two natural facilities
  b two outdoor built facilities
  c two indoor built facilities
  d one facility provided by private enterprise
  e two provided by voluntary organizations
  f two provided by the local authority

10 Suppose you are a local authority planner. You want to develop the lake in question 9 as a recreational facility.
  a Suggest some activities that could take place there.
  b List all the different groups that might use the lake.
  c Identify any conflicts that might arise between the activities. What steps could you take to avoid them?
  d If you can come up with a project that involves the local community and the school, you might obtain a Lottery Sports Fund grant. Suggest a suitable project.
  e Will you need to build anything round the lake? What? Why?

11 What factors must be taken into consideration when deciding where facilities are to be located?

12 Some people object to facilities being built in certain places. Why might this be the case?

13 Some schools offer a wide range of sports. Others offer very few.

    a Name three things that affect how much sport a school can offer.

    b What special problems might schools in inner-cities face with respect to facilities?

    c Explain how a school could offer:

      i tennis, even though it has no tennis courts

      ii climbing, even though it is an inner-city school.

    d What might help the school do the things you suggested in **c**?

14 What does PESSCL stand for and how does it help create sporting opportunities for school children?

15 Explain how PESSCL encourages schools to work together.

16 What is the 5x60 initiative in Welsh schools?

17 Apart from PE and sport, what other things does a school do to encourage you to adopt a healthy lifestyle?

18 In school you are encouraged to adopt different roles as part of your PE programme.

    a Name the different roles you could take up.

    b What are the benefits of adopting different roles?

19 In what ways do schools use media to make learning easier and more fun?

APPLIED QUESTIONS

A20 Sarah is a 15-year-old girl who is unfit but wants to be fitter. She enjoys most indoor sports and has recently started to train regularly. Her parents both drive but do not have the time to take her to the local sports centre where she can use the facilities cheaply.

    a What level of the sports participation pyramid is Sarah on? Explain your answer.

    b What effect on her participation are her parents likely to have?

    c How might her school help her participate more?

THINGS TO DO

A survey of local facilities.

    a List the facilities for sport and physical recreation in your area within a radius of 5km of your school or home (Yellow Pages or the local Thomson directory will help).

    b For each facility, find out whether it is provided by the local council, private enterprise, a voluntary organisation, or a national authority.

A detailed survey of one facility

You may want to work with a partner for this. Choose a local sports or recreational facility. Contact the manager and ask if you can visit the facility as part of a school survey. Find out the answers to these questions.

    a What activities does it offer?

    b Which different groups of people use it? For example, does it welcome disabled people, or mothers with toddlers?

    c What provision does it make for the different groups? For example, is there a crèche?

    d How much does it cost to use? Find out all the different charge rates. For example:

      i is it less to get in if you become a member?

      ii how much does membership cost?

      iii are there different rates for the unemployed? families? the over fifties? retired people? students?

      iv are there different rates for different times of day? Would a person in a wheelchair have any problems in moving around the facility? Walk around and check for ramps, swing doors and so on.

    e Does the facility offer social areas such as a cafe or bar? Now write a report for the class about the facility.

Ask the manager if you can perform a survey on the customers at the centre and devise a questionnaire. Here are some examples of questions you could ask but you might want to think of some of your own:

    1. Is the customer male or female?

    2. What age bracket do they fit in?

    3. Which of the facilities here do they use?

    4. When do they use the facilities most often: morning, afternoon or evening?

    5. What days of the week do they use the centre?

When you have all your results, use a spreadsheet to illustrate the information.

The manager of the centre will probably be very interested to see them.

12.1 ORGANISATIONS

•••• In this unit you will learn about the work of some sports organisations and how they promote physical activity.

THE SPORTS COUNCILS

There are in fact five Sports Councils: UK Sport, Sport England, Sport Scotland, Sports Council for Wales and Sports Council for Northern Ireland.

Sport England, along with the government, is pursuing two main aims: to get everyone active and to make England successful. The Start, Stay, Succeed initiative showed their vision for sport:

◎ Start – increase participation in sport in order to improve the health of the nation, particularly females, ethnic minorities, those with disabilities and those in the lowest socio-economic group.

◎ Stay – retain people in sport through an effective network of clubs, facilities, coaches, volunteers and competitive opportunities.

◎ Succeed – create opportunities for talented performers to achieve success.

Sport England now has a strategy called Grow Sustain Excel to get more people playing and enjoying sport and to help those with talent to reach the highest levels. Backed by the government and carried out in association with many other organisations, this strategy sets demanding targets for Sport England to deliver for 2012 and 2013. The government is investing a lot of money in sport and so it wants to see results but after the Olympic success of 2008 it looks like that is already being delivered.

NATIONAL GOVERNING BODIES

Each organised sport has a national governing body. Examples are the Football Association and the All England Netball Association. These bodies are responsible for:

◎ drawing up the rules of the sport and preventing their abuse
◎ organising local and national competitions
◎ selecting teams for international competitions, for example, European and World Championships
◎ settling disputes within the sport
◎ managing and coaching referees and umpires
◎ helping to develop facilities
◎ maintaining links with similar organisations abroad.

The governing body usually consists of all the regional and county associations, and leagues if they exist. These elect a central council to run it. The county associations in turn represent the local clubs. The governing body has links with similar governing bodies in other countries, and with the European and World governing bodies.

To finance its work, the governing body raises funds from major sporting events, members' subscriptions, sponsorship, grants from UK Sport and The Lottery Sports Fund, and where possible selling broadcast rights for events to radio and TV.

In unit 11.1 you learned about the Sports Participation Pyramid and how elite performers develop from a wide base of participators. The organisations that produce top performers are therefore keen to get everyone taking part.

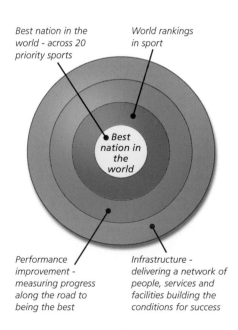

Best nation in the world - across 20 priority sports

World rankings in sport

Best nation in the world

Performance improvement - measuring progress along the road to being the best

Infrastructure - delivering a network of people, services and facilities building the conditions for success

One of Sport England's bulls-eye targets for sport.

THE INTERNATIONAL OLYMPIC COMMITTEE (IOC)

This is the top committee of the Olympic Movement. It is chosen from member countries. Its main jobs are:
◎ to select the cities where the Games will be held
◎ to decide which sports will be included
◎ to work with the host city and other bodies to plan the Games
◎ to lead the fight against doping in sport.

For funding, the IOC depends mainly on the sale of TV rights and on sponsorship by multinationals such as Coca-Cola and Samsung. TV companies across the world pay billions of pounds for the broadcast rights to the Olympic Games. Sponsors are not allowed to advertise in the Olympic stadiums, but they can use the Olympic symbols on their products. They get access to exclusive hospitality at the Games, and to the best advertising slots when the games are broadcast.

The money the IOC receives is divided up between the IOC, the International Sports Federations, the National Olympic Committees, and the local Organizing Committee for each Olympics.

CITIUS · ALTIUS · FORTIUS

The logo and motto of the International Olympic Committee (IOC).

THE BRITISH OLYMPIC ASSOCIATION (BOA)

The BOA is part of the Olympic Movement. Its main jobs are:
◎ To select, with the governing bodies, Team GB.
◎ To meet the needs of Team GB, including medical advice.
◎ To help athletes balance their sport with other aspects of their life.
◎ To assist athletes to establish a career alongside their sport.
◎ To give athletes reduced cost access to local and national facilities.
◎ To give athletes advice from experienced Olympians.
◎ To run the Olympic Training centre for high performance athletes.

The BOA also selects and prepares the British Youth Olympic Team. This team competes at the European Youth Olympic Festival and at the bi-annual Australian Youth Olympic festival. This gives top young sports people a taste of what might be in the future for them. They also receive medical support, free use of local facilities and career and education services arranged by the BOA.

The BOA gets some money from the IOC, but not nearly enough to support the team. It raises most of its funding from sponsorship, licensing its logo and donations from the public. It also has links with businesses that support a particular sport by giving them 'support in kind'. The BOA is not controlled or funded by the government, which means the government cannot tell them what to do.

The logo of the British Olympic Association.

QUESTIONS

1 **a** How many Sports Councils are there?
  b Name the governing body of the area in which you live.

2 What does the governing body of a sport do?

3 How does a governing body encourage people to participate either as a performer, coach or official?

4 What do the initials IOC and BOA stand for?

5 How do the IOC and BOA get most of their funding?

Discussion work

6 It is important that the Olympic organisations do not get involved in politics. Why?

12.2 FUNDING SPORT

In this unit you will learn about where the money comes from to run sport.

It costs a lot to build and run sports facilities, organise events, buy equipment and train athletes. Who pays?

WHERE DOES THE MONEY COME FROM?

National government. The government raises money each year from taxes and other sources. Then at Budget time the Chancellor decides how much can be spent, and divides it among the different government departments. The Department for Culture, Media and Sport is responsible for sport. It decides how much of its share will go to sport. Most of this is divided among the five **Sports Councils.** They use the money to help develop sport, improve facilities and promote excellence. In 2007–2008 the government spent an estimated £190.9 million on sport. You can find out more about the Sports Councils in unit 12.1.

Local government. Your local council raises money by means of the **council tax** which each household pays, and the **business tax** paid by shops and other businesses. It uses the money to build and maintain schools and recreational facilities as well as for services such as the police, fire service and refuse disposal.

The governing bodies of sport. They earn money from things like selling permission for events to be broadcast on TV and radio. For example the Football Association made a TV deal worth £743 million in 1997. They also sell tickets for major events such as cup finals and Wimbledon. They then plough most of the money back into their sports.

The National Lottery. The National Lottery was launched in 1994. Every week we spend an average of £5.35 per household on National Lottery tickets. From the sale of each ticket 28p goes to good causes. In 2007 half of this went to health, education, environment, community and charity causes whilst the other half was shared equally between sport, arts and heritage. The Lottery Sports Fund is handled by the Sports Councils who award it as grants for sports projects.

Sponsorship. This is a big source of finance for sport. For example:
◎ Adidas sponsor basketball in the community.
◎ Barclays sponsor Premier League football matches.

But sponsorship isn't just for big projects and big names. A local business might pay for a trophy or the strip for the local junior football team. There is more about sponsorship on pages 62–63.

Private individuals. A wealthy person may donate a large sum to a favourite club, or even buy it! Mohammed Al Fayed, businessman and owner of Harrods, is owner of Fulham Football Club.

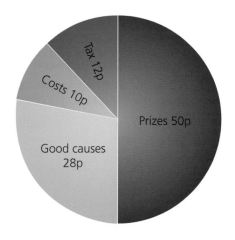

A National Lottery ticket: where the £1 goes.

Sales of tickets and merchandise. Clubs get money by selling tickets to events, and things like sweat shirts, scarves, flags and posters.

Membership fees. Small clubs like the local squash club charge a membership fee to cover running expenses.

MORE ABOUT TAXATION

These are the kinds of taxes we pay the government:
◎ **a tax on earnings.** Individual earners pay **income tax**. Businesses pay **corporation tax**. The more you earn the more you pay. Even bodies like the Lawn Tennis Association and Football Association have to pay tax.
◎ **a tax on spending.** A tax called **value added tax** (VAT) is included in the price of most things you buy. For example, in the price of CDs, computer games and petrol, and on your phone bill.

Each year the Treasury takes in billions from the taxation of sport. It gives nowhere near that much back to sport.

Every time you buy a replica kit or other merchandise, a percentage goes to the government as VAT. Do they always spend it on sport?

THE LOTTERY SPORTS FUND

The projects can be large or small: from £120 million to build the new Wembley stadium to individual athlete personal awards of £50. Suppose a youth club wants to build a new clubhouse. It can apply to the Lottery Sports Fund for a grant. The application goes to a panel which says yes or no. A project will receive funding only if:
◎ it will benefit the community, including disabled people.
◎ it involves building or improving something or buying equipment.
◎ it is well thought out and likely to succeed.
◎ a 'significant' amount of the total cost will be raised elsewhere.

The projects can be large or small. In 1996 Welsh Rugby Union was awarded £46 million to build a new stadium and complex in Cardiff. Average grants are usually around £40 000, however.

WHO CAN APPLY FOR A LOTTERY SPORTS FUND GRANT?

Organisations like these:
• sports clubs
• youth clubs
• community associations
• sports associations
• governing bodies of sport
• local authorities
• schools and colleges (for facilities they intend to share with the public).

QUESTIONS

1 Explain how sport is funded by: **a** national government **b** local government.
2 When a person spends £1 on a lottery ticket, where does the money go?
3 Describe three taxes levied by the government.
4 Which bodies look after the Lottery Sports Fund?

5 Think up a sports project for a local youth club which could qualify for lottery funding. How will it benefit the local community, including disabled people? Describe it as fully as you can.

Discussion work

6 Some people think that lottery money should not be spent on things like education. Why? What is your opinion?

12.3   INTERNATIONAL SPORT

●●●● In this unit you will learn about the organisation of international sports events.

THE BENEFITS OF INTERNATIONAL SPORT

◎ It gives players and supporters from different countries the chance to meet and develop friendship.

◎ It unites people from different races, religions, cultures and classes in a shared interest.

◎ It gives the world's top athletes the chance to compete against each other. This encourages excellence.

◎ It spreads interest in sport and encourages more people to play.

INTERNATIONAL AND HIGH PROFILE EVENTS

Most sports hold international events arranged by their international governing bodies. For example, FIFA arrange the Football World Cup, FINA arrange the World Swimming Championships. Other sports hold a series of events such as Test Matches between countries, as in cricket, or Grand Slam tennis competitions such as Wimbledon.

Events such as the Commonwealth Games and the Olympics cover a wide range of sports. They are arranged by separate organisations with help from the governing bodies. For example the International Olympic Committee unit 12.1) arranges the Summer and Winter Olympics and the Paralympics.

HOSTING INTERNATIONAL EVENTS

The host is the city or country staging the events. The venue is the stadium where an event is held. The Olympics are hosted by cities – for example Beijing in 2008. But many events are hosted by countries and spread around several centres. Germany was the host of the 2006 Football World Cup with venues in 12 cities across the country including Berlin, Hamburg and Munich.

SOME ADVANTAGES OF PLAYING HOST

Countries and cities often compete fiercely for the chance to host an international sports event. Why?

◎ For prestige. It is considered an honour to host the Olympics. If the event is a success, the host city gains prestige. This can pay in all kinds of ways, including an increase in trade and tourism.

◎ It unites the country and gives a sense of pride.

◎ It gives a boost to sports facilities – and other facilities. Cities build or improve their facilities to host events. The local people can enjoy these long after the events are over.

◎ The event may make a profit. Sales of radio and TV rights, tickets and merchandise can bring in a lot of money. Local shops, restaurants, hotels, taxis and other services will also benefit.

○ **THE OLYMPIC IDEALS**
The aim of the Olympics is to promote:
- personal excellence
- sport as education
- cultural exchange
- mass participation
- fair play
- international understanding.

High profile events:
- The Premiership
- The Superbowl
- The British Open
- Formula One
- The Americas Cup
- The Tri-Nations.
- But what sport is each for?

SOME DISADVANTAGES OF PLAYING HOST

◎ If it runs into problems in organising an event, the country or city may lose money. Montreal made a loss of over $1 billion with the Olympic Games in 1976. The debt took 30 years to pay off!

◎ An event that attracts hooligans puts a big strain on the police. They may have to patrol trains and airports as well as venues.

◎ A large number of visitors means extra strain on hotels, transport, water supplies and so on. If these can't cope there will be problems.

◎ Big events are security risks. They are watched by millions, so terrorists and other groups may use them to air their grievances. They may be disrupted by bomb threats, strikes and riots, e.g. the bombing at the Atlanta Olympics in Centennial Park, where two people were killed and 110 injured.

◎ If an event does not go well the host's image suffers. The host will have difficulty attracting other events.

China spent millions building these facilities. Could the money have been better spent on other things for the country?

INTERNATIONAL SPORT AND POLITICS

Sport can promote peace and understanding. But where countries are already enemies, they may use it as a form of 'cold war'.

◎ A country may decide to boycott an event for political reasons.

◎ It may use its top athletes to prove it is more powerful than its enemy, or that its political system is superior.

The Olympic Games are the world's biggest and most spectacular sports event. Over the years they have often been used for political purposes. For example, in Munich in 1972, 11 Israeli team members were killed when Palestinian terrorists broke into the Olympic village and took them hostage. The terrorists wanted the release of 200 Palestinians held in Israeli prisons.

INTERNATIONAL SPORT AND MONEY

It can be wildly expensive to stage an international event. This means:

◎ poor countries just can't afford them.

◎ even the rich countries can't afford major events without sponsorship and the sale of broadcast rights. For example, it cost over $2 billion to stage the Sydney Olympics, $15 billion for Athens.

Some people think that the Olympics are now too commercial, with entertainment and profit as important as sport. What do you think?

QUESTIONS

1 Write down two benefits of international sport.

2 Name a city that has hosted: **a** the Summer Olympics **b** the Winter Olympics **c** the Commonwealth Games.

3 a Write down two advantages of hosting an international sports event. **b** Now write down two disadvantages.

Discussion work

4 Why is it important that events such as the Olympic Games become increasingly 'green'?

155

12.4 THE OLYMPIC GAMES AND 2012

• • • • • In this unit you will learn about the Olympic Games and issues relating to London 2012.

A BRIEF HISTORY OF THE OLYMPICS

The modern Olympic Games are based on the old games of Ancient Greece which were held every four years as part of a religious ceremony to the god Zeus. At the end of the 19th century, Baron Pierre de Coubertin had the idea of reintroducing the games and in 1896 the first games of the modern era were held in Greece. Since then, with the exception of two breaks because of world wars, the Games have been held every four years. Over the years the Games have grown and they are now probably the most important sporting competition in the world.

As the Games grew, and particularly as they received increased media attention, the Olympics became linked with more political issues. Sometimes the Games are remembered more for the issues surrounding them than for the events themselves!

Athens 1896	Beijing 2008
43 events	302 events
14 nations	203 nations
241 competitors	Over 10,500 competitors

How the Games have grown!

ENVIRONMENTAL ISSUES

Sport is increasingly becoming concerned with environmental issues. In order to host the Olympic Games a city must show that the Games will have a positive impact on green issues, such as being carbon neutral, blending facilities into the environment or revitalising poor or run-down areas of the city in an environmentally friendly way. It is important that all the money that is invested builds a future for the host city. This is one reason why a host city is chosen six years in advance and the preparations for the bid also take many years.

Unfortunately not every host city's preparations go to plan and after their Games are over, some host cities have facilities that are rarely used and they have huge debts to pay off!

These facilities will cost millions to build but how much use will they get after the Games? Is this a good use of money?

LONDON 2012

In 2005, after two years of campaigning, London won the bid to host the Olympic and Paralympic Games of 2012 and at the closing ceremony of the Beijing Olympics, London officially received the Olympic flag and became the new Olympic city. When the bid was won, 60% of the facilities were already in place, the rest would have to be built specially for the Games. The main venue is in the Stratford area of East London, but events will also be held across the UK, including in Glasgow and Belfast. Famous landmarks like the Millennium Dome, Lord's Cricket Ground and Wembley Stadium will all be used to host events. One of the biggest concerns surrounding London's bid was the transport problems for spectators. Most of the athletes will be accommodated close to their venues but spectators will be arriving from all directions and from all corners of the world. London has promised to improve public transport in time for the Games.

Not everyone is happy about the Olympics coming to London. Local people have had to pay an extra £20 on their Council Tax to help fund the Games and some local businesses have been closed to make way for new facilities. When the Games take place people living nearby are going to feel that their community has been taken over! It is hoped, however, that the Olympics will leave behind a legacy that will benefit the people of East London for years to come.

FUNDING 2012

There is no doubt that hosting the Olympic Games is expensive; Beijing reportedly cost £20 billion! When London won the bid the projected cost was £2.4 billion but by 2007 it had risen to £9.4 billion and in 2008 it was thought that it might be even higher. So where does the money come from?

A lot of money comes from sponsorship and selling TV rights but a large amount for 2012 will come from the National Lottery. The National Lottery has always made a significant contribution to charities, cultural and sporting organisations so that of each £1 ticket sold, 28p goes to good causes. In 2005 Camelot, the company that runs the Lottery, launched new games specifically to raise funds for 2012. All of the good cause money from Dream Number and Olympic scratch cards will go to the Games and it is expected to raise £1.5 billion.

The logo of the 2012 Olympic Games.

Cost and income for the Games estimated at the time of London's bid. Some of these figures have risen dramatically since the bid!

Projected costs	£	Expected revenue	£
Venues	560 million	National Lottery	1.5 billion
Olympic Village	650 million	Council Tax	625 million
Running costs	1.5 billion	TV and marketing	560 million
Security	200 million	Sponsorship	450 million
		Ticket sales	300 million
		London Development Agency	250 million
		Licensing	60 million
Totals	2.91 billion		3.745 billion

In 2007 the government promised £6 billion towards the cost of the Games. As a result of the Games being staged in London, Team GB will have the excitement of performing in front of a home crowd and we will have the opportunity to see the Games live. In Beijing the UK won 47 medals, 19 of them gold; it is hoped that London 2012 will be even more successful for us.

QUESTIONS

1 Name three ways in which the Olympic Games can be made to be more environmentally friendly.

2 How is staging the Olympics expected to benefit the host city?

3 Local people may not welcome the Games being staged in their area. Why?

4 How much of a lottery ticket goes to good causes?

5 Give four ways in which funding for the Games is raised.

Discussion work

6 How is the preparation for 2012 going?

7 Do you think the London Games will be successful? What would successful mean for you?

8 Do you agree with the amount of money being spent on the Games?

QUESTIONS ON CHAPTER 12

1 What do these initials stand for?
   a IOC   b BOA
   c FIFA   d AENA

2 What are the main jobs of the IOC and BOA?

3 Why might the BOA be interested in promoting sport at grass roots level?

4 How many sports councils are there and what are they called?

5 Sport England introduced a policy for sport called Start, Stay, Succeed. What does each word mean in relation to sports participation?

6 What are the target groups of the Start, Stay, Succeed initiative?

7 Sport England has a new strategy for sport leading up to 2013. What is it called?

8 How does the governing body of a sport raise funds?

9 Name five national governing bodies including the one for your sport.

10 The Football Association (FA) is the governing body for football in England.
   a Name the world governing body for football.
   b Name the European governing body.
   c List four functions of a governing body.

11 Funding is essential if athletes are to become top performers. Name five sources of funding.

12 This shows how much the local tennis club expects to spend in the coming year:

	£
Redecoration of the club house	1800
Repairs to courts	800
New nets	1700
Coaching fees	800
Groundsman	1000
Insurance	550
Post and phone	450
	7100

   a The club has 70 members. It charges £30 a year for membership. How much money does that bring in?
   b It costs £4.50 to book a court. Last year there were 1000 bookings. How much did that bring in?
   c Suppose the bookings remain at the same level next year. How much more money will the club need to find, to cover its costs for the year?
   d You are the club treasurer. You are determined that the club will not make a loss next year. Write a list of suggestions for ways to raise money, which you will present at the next committee meeting.

13 This chart shows where each £1 from a lottery ticket goes. You can assume that the money from scratch cards is divided in the same way. (It is very similar.)

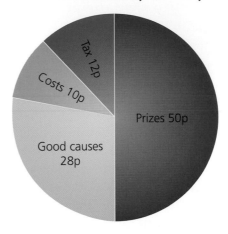

   a How much goes to good causes including sport?
   b Where does most of the money go?
   c Write a paragraph in favour of the National Lottery, showing how it benefits society. Give examples.
   d Now write a paragraph describing its harmful effects.
   e Overall, are you in favour of the Lottery or against it?

14 Organisations can apply for Lottery Sports Grants.
   a What kind of organisations can apply?
   b What conditions must they meet before a grant is awarded?

15 a Even though you don't earn, you still pay tax now and then, for example when you buy a CD. Explain this.
   b Working people pay a tax that depends on the size of their income. What is it called?
   c Households also pay a tax.
      i What is this tax called?
      ii Who collects it?
      iii Name three things the money is used for.

16 What are some of the problems associated with hosting an international sports event? Give your answer in relation to:
   a Politics
   b Finance.

17 Why do international events such as the Olympic Games sometimes 'attract' trouble?

18 Hosting the Olympic Games is extremely expensive. What are the main things a host city needs to spend money on?

19 Some people think that companies like McDonalds and Coca-Cola should not sponsor the Olympic Games. Why do you think this is the case?

20 How can a city make money hosting the Olympic Games?

21 The Olympic Games are supposed to leave behind a legacy. What does this mean?

APPLIED QUESTION

A22 Jemma is a successful professional athlete who trains full time in order to compete in the marathon for England and Great Britain. She hopes to be part of the 2012 Olympic team.

  a What organisations will be helping her?

  b Apart from sponsorship, what other funding might she receive?

  c The 2012 Olympics are being held in London. How will this benefit Jemma?

THINGS TO DO

Competitions
Different sports hold different types of competition. Get your class to organise some using some of these methods:

Ladder
All the competitors are placed in rank order according to ability. Each player can challenge players 1 or 2 places above him or her. If he or she wins he or she goes up a place, if he or she loses the positions stay the same. The winner is the person at the top of the ladder after a certain amount of time.

League
Like a football league, each team plays all the other teams once or twice in a **round robin**. Points are awarded for a win or a draw. The winning team is the one with most points at the end of the competition.

Knockout
Like Wimbledon, a draw takes place to decide who plays whom in the first round. The winners go through to the next round and so on until there are only two players or teams left who then battle it out in the final.

Qualification
Like the European Cup in football or the triple jump event in the Olympics, in order to get through to the final stage, competitors must qualify first. They do this either by playing in qualifying rounds or by achieving a set standard, depending on the sport.

USE OF INFORMATION TECHNOLOGY

1 Several organisations have been described in this chapter. Divide them up amongst the members of your class and look for more information on the internet about each one.

2 Use the internet to research some of the problems associated with the Games. Use the following keywords to focus your search:

  a Olympics + Berlin

  b Olympics + Black power

  c Olympics + Munich

  d Olympics + Tibet or Olympics + Chinese human rights.

3 Use the internet to research the preparation for London 2012. Try to find out:

  a Whereabouts the individual sports will be based.

  b How many new facilities are being/have been built.

  c Whether the facilities are expected to be finished on time.

  d How much money has been raised through lottery funding.

  e What is being done to improve transport to the venues.

  f What is being done to help prepare our athletes.

  g How much funding each individual sport has been given to help prepare the team.

  h How many medals Team GB hopes to win and in which sports.

  i What the Games will cost. Compare this with the original estimate.

13.1   AMATEUR OR PROFESSIONAL

In this unit you will learn about the differences between amateur and professional sports performers.

How do you tell who's amateur and who's not? The term **amateur** was originally a sign of social class. It meant you were a gentleman who could afford to play a sport just for pleasure. There's more about this on page 166.

◉ Amateurs do not get paid for playing their sport. The theory is they do it for love of the sport.

◉ Professionals play full time and get paid for it: it's their living.

◉ Semi-professionals are like professionals but play only part time and have another job too.

WHO DECIDES?

The rules about amateurs and professionals, and what they can and can't do, are made by a sport's international governing body.

◉ Many sports divide players clearly into professionals and amateurs, with the professionals at the top. Football is an example. Amateurs and professionals don't usually compete together, except in specific events. For example, amateur, semi-professional and professional football teams can compete in the FA Cup.

◉ In some sports most athletes, even the top ones, are 'amateur'. Swimming and athletics are examples. The athletes can't accept money for playing their sports. But see below for ways around this!

◉ Some sports are open. Amateurs and professionals can compete freely in most events. Horse racing, golf and tennis are examples.

ARE TOP AMATEURS REALLY NOT PAID?

To be a top athlete you need to devote yourself full time to your sport. But if you're not allowed to earn money from it, how do you survive?

Scholarships. In America young athletes get scholarships to colleges with a good reputation for their chosen sport. Scholarships can cover everything: food, board, books and tuition. The athletes train with top coaches in top facilities. They don't have to worry about money. Several UK universities now offer sports scholarships.

'Jobs'. In many countries athletes are given token 'jobs', for example as PE instructors in the army or police force, so that they can train full time. This often happens in developing countries.

Special training camps. Promising young athletes may be sent to sports schools and then training camps, where they remain long past the age when most people get a job. This is usual in China.

Trust funds. In the past, athletes in athletics could only accept prize and appearance money, but not directly. It was paid into a **trust fund** in order to preserve their amateur status. Money from the fund was used to cover the athlete's training and living expenses. He or she got the rest on retirement. This is no longer the case now that athletics is fully professional.

In unit 11.1 you saw that people can follow a vocation in sport, here we look more closely at professional sport.

SOME FOOTBALL TEAMS

Professional
Newcastle United
Tottenham Hotspur
and similar league teams

Semi-professional
Kettering Town
Ebbsfleet United
and similar non-league teams

Amateur
Your local Sunday team

SOME OPEN SPORTS

angling	mountaineering
bowling	squash
cricket	tennis

Grants and sponsorships. Amateur athletes can seek grants from Sports Aid, for example, or sponsorship from business. The governing bodies must approve these.

WHY KEEP THE DISTINCTION?

As you can see, top 'amateur' athletes get 'paid' indirectly in all kinds of ways. So the distinction between amateurs and professionals is a fuzzy one. Why not just drop it and make all sports open?

The fear is that money would then become the main reason for competing, with athletes aiming to win at all costs and by any methods.
The ideal of fair play might go out the window. Governing bodies might lose control of their sports to commercial organisations.

AMATEURISM AND THE OLYMPIC GAMES

The Olympic Games were meant for amateurs. Tennis was dropped in the 1920s because of doubts about the players' status.

But over the years it has been obvious that many competitors are not truly amateur, and many winners were rewarded when they got home, for example with cars, jobs and houses. In 1981 the term 'Olympic amateur' was dropped from the rules. Tennis, with professional players, was allowed back in 1988. But the only prizes offered at the Olympics are the Olympic medals.

The final decision about who can take part in the games is now left to the International Sports Federations. Some sports uphold the amateur ideal more strictly than others. For example professional footballers can now take part in the games but professional boxers cannot.

THE STORY OF RUGBY LEAGUE AND RUGBY UNION

Rugby began at Rugby School. The rules were laid down in 1846. By 1881 Rugby Union governing bodies had been set up in England, Scotland and Wales.

But in 1895 Rugby League was born when 22 northern clubs broke away. Their players wanted compensation for the time spent away from work training and playing. Rugby Union had refused them.

Rugby League became the professional game, and developed its own rules over the years. Then in 1995, a hundred years later, Rugby Union finally backed down and let professional players in.

This worldwide game began life on the playing fields of England.

QUESTIONS

1 What is an **amateur** athlete? Name one top athlete who has amateur status.

2 What is a **professional** athlete? Name four.

3 What is an **open** sport? Name four.

4 To remain 'amateur', athletes must not earn a living from their sport. Describe three 'loop holes' that allow them to get round this.

Discussion work

5 Do you think allowing professional athletes in all sports is a good thing? Try to come up with a list of positive and negative points for both sides of the argument.

13.2 SPONSORSHIP

● ● ● ●   In this unit you will learn how sponsorship has an impact on sport.

WHAT IS SPONSORSHIP?

Without a sponsor, many athletes couldn't carry on with their sport. **Sponsorship** is where a business provides support (usually financial) for an event or team or athlete. Watch sport on TV and you'll see sponsors' brand names on players' clothing and hoardings around the venues.

WHY SPONSOR SPORT?

◎ It is a way to advertise. The sponsor's name is displayed before the spectators all through the event.

◎ Sport has a healthy, positive image. Businesses like to be associated with this.

◎ Sponsorship is often **tax-deductible**. This means the business does not have to pay tax on the amount it spends on sponsorship. (That is one way the government helps to promote sport.)

◎ TV sports events are seen in millions of homes. So is the sponsor's brand name. An event like Wimbledon or a Cup Final reaches millions of TV screens round the world. This means a sponsor's logo reaches places that may be very difficult or expensive to reach with other kinds of advertising.

◎ When a local business sponsors a local team, it gains the good will of the local people.

◎ In exchange for sponsorship a sponsor may get the best seats at an event, or the use of luxury executive boxes. The sponsor can use these to entertain clients.

DISADVANTAGES TO THE SPONSOR

◎ The sponsor expects the athlete or team to behave well, or the event to go smoothly. This cannot be guaranteed. If an event is disrupted by hooliganism or the weather, or an athlete is caught doping or cheating, or gets involved in a scandal, the sponsor won't be happy.

◎ The sponsor also hopes the team or athlete will be successful. That can't be guaranteed either.

FORMS OF SPONSORSHIP

Sponsorship may be for:

◎ a sport. Norwich Union, amongst others, sponsors UK Athletics.

◎ a single event. Flora sponsors the London Marathon.

◎ a team. AIG sponsors Manchester United. So do several other companies, as you'll see if you check out the players' kit.

◎ An individual. Michael Phelps is sponsored by Speedo and won a $1 million bonus when, at the 2008 Olympics, he equalled Mark Spitz's record 7 gold medals. (He went on to win 8!)

Sponsorship is not always money. A car manufacturer may provide free transport, and an airline free flights. A company that makes sports goods may provide clothing and equipment. Sponsorship for a young person could be in the form of a scholarship to a centre of excellence.

The London Marathon, sponsored mainly by Flora. You can usually tell from the size of the banners which company has provided most sponsorship.

For the 2008/09 season, Aston Villa gave their shirt sponsorship to a charity for free.

FINDING SPONSORSHIP

It can be hard for an unknown young athlete to find sponsorship. Sponsors like a safe bet! Athletes, coaches and agents spend a lot of time calling on companies and very often the answer is no.

A sport may have difficulty finding sponsorship if it doesn't have a slot on TV. Big sponsors like high profile TV sports. Far more people watch sports on TV than at live venues.

It can be especially difficult for female or black athletes. Sponsors who make computers and upmarket cars aim their ads at the spectators with most spending power. These tend to be youngish, white and male. The sponsors go for the favourite sports, events and stars of this group.

But if you're a sports star you'll have no problem getting sponsorship. Companies will queue up to pay you to endorse their products: to wear their clothing, drink their soft drinks or drive their cars. Top athletes can earn more from these deals than from their sport.

Sports stars can earn a lot of money just by taking a sip from a sponsor's soft drink during a match. Wearing a sponsor's clothing or sports shoes can earn them a whole lot more. They must be careful not to be seen with a rival company's products!

THE BENEFITS AND DRAWBACKS FOR SPORT

Benefits for sport

◎ To promote and develop a sport you need to stage events. This can be very expensive. Sponsorship makes it possible.

◎ Sponsorship also helps talented athletes to train and compete when they couldn't otherwise afford to.

◎ For top athletes, it can be very lucrative. This is useful because their careers may be short.

Drawbacks for sport

◎ A deal lasts only a certain time. It does not give a team or an athlete long-term security.

◎ A sponsor may be bad for a sport's image. Sponsorship by alcohol and tobacco companies is not allowed for events for the under-18s. There is also pressure on TV companies to stop broadcasting events that are sponsored by tobacco companies.

◎ Sponsors may want to dictate the timing of sports events to suit their own purposes. For example to coincide with peak viewing time on TV. This might not be best for the athletes.

◎ Teams and athletes may feel exploited by sponsors. This can lower their satisfaction with sport and their motivation to succeed.

QUESTIONS

1 What is **sponsorship**?

2 Describe two benefits to the sponsor.

3 Now describe two possible problems for the sponsor.

4 Give two other real-life examples (not used here) of sponsorship for: **a** a team **b** an individual

5 Female rugby teams have particular difficulty in obtaining sponsorship. Try to explain why.

6 Give one benefit and one drawback of sponsorship for: **a** a team **b** an individual

Discussion work

7 On balance, is sponsorship a good idea? Why?

13.3 SPORT AND THE MEDIA

● ● ● ● In this unit you will learn how the media have an impact on sport. Some of the effects are good, but not all!

The media are all the means by which information is delivered to you: books, newspapers, magazines, radio, TV, cinema and video.

HOW THE MEDIA AFFECT SPORT

The media have an enormous impact on sport. This is particularly true of TV. Some of the effects are good, some not!

Positive effects

◎ The media help to promote sport. Sporting events are seen, heard and read about by millions of people.
◎ They create sports 'stars' who may inspire young athletes. David Beckham, the star of European football, became an American idol when he moved to the USA.
◎ When a sport gets a lot of media attention, more people get interested in playing it.
◎ Sports that get a lot of media coverage, especially on TV, find it easier to obtain sponsorship.
◎ The media can educate and inform you about sport. For example, through documentaries, coaching programmes and discussion of current issues. It helps to give you an understanding of performance and participation.
◎ TV companies pay large sums to the governing bodies of sport for the right to broadcast events. This is used to develop the sport.

Dance and other activities also benefit from the media in these ways.

Some drawbacks

◎ Media exposure may foster the desire to win at all costs rather than play for enjoyment.
◎ There is more pressure on managers and team captains to get results. The media may hound them out of their jobs if they fail.
◎ Sports stars lose privacy. Their private lives get reported on.
◎ TV may encourage rule changes. Formula 1 stopped tyre changes during races in the hope that the races would become more exciting for TV viewers. The tie break in tennis was introduced to appeal to a TV audience.
◎ The media may over-sensationalise events. Why would they do this?

HOW THE MEDIA PRESENT SPORT

When you read about something in the paper, or watch it on TV, or listen on the radio, it is *not* like being there yourself. The event has been 'packaged' for you by the people working in the medium. They have decided what to put in, what to leave out, and what point of view to take. For example, in TV sports the camera operators and video editors decide which shots you see and from which angle. The producers decide who should be interviewed. The interviewers decide which questions to ask.

Media attention can make sportspeople into household names.

What you see is often *more* exciting than the actual event, thanks to close-up shots, slow-motion replays, interviews and a dramatic commentary. In real life you would not hear a player's thoughts before a match, or see the pain on a manager's face as his team loses.

In all of the media, the way an event is packaged depends on how much time, space and money is available. But it also depends on which of these things the media makers intend to do:

◎ entertain you
◎ inform you
◎ educate you
◎ 'hype' an event
◎ attract attention (and sales) by being sensational
◎ please the sponsors
◎ express a particular point of view.

NEWSPAPERS

Newspapers like sport because it helps to sell them. It also attracts advertising. Some companies advertise their products in the sports pages.

When our sportsmen and sportswomen do well they are the focus of much media attention.

The tabloid press includes *The Daily Mirror*, *The Sun* and the *Daily Express*. The quality press includes *The Independent*, *Times*, *Guardian* and *Daily Telegraph*. Both cover sports, but there are differences:

The tabloids tend to . . .	The quality press tends to . . .
go for sensational headlines	go for in-depth coverage and comment
take a strong line of approval or disapproval	do more thoughtful analysis
pay little attention to minority sports	give more coverage to minority sports

THE INTERNET

The use of the internet is rapidly increasing. In 2007 61% of households in the UK had internet access; a 7% increase on 2006. The internet gives you the opportunity to:

◎ Download TV events you may have missed.
◎ Catch up on recent events and results.
◎ Find out details of upcoming events and fixtures.
◎ Find out details of how and where you can take up a sport.
◎ Access websites of newspapers and radio for sports-related articles.

QUESTIONS

1 What is meant by the media?

2 List three ways in which media coverage helps sport.

3 Describe three drawbacks of media coverage.

4 Several people play a part in selecting and shaping the information you receive in a sports programme. Name three of them.

5 Give one example of a TV sports programme designed mainly to entertain.

6 Name: **a** one tabloid **b** one quality paper.

Discussion work

7 Sports stars often accuse the media of invading their privacy. Do you think we have the right to know things about their private lives?

13.4   MORE ABOUT SPORT AND TV

In this unit you will learn specifically about the role of TV in sport.

HOW SPORT BENEFITS TV

Of all the media, TV has the biggest impact on sport – and vice versa!
You saw in the last unit how TV and other media benefit sport.
Now look at the way sport benefits TV:

◉ It is often shown at times when TV would otherwise have few viewers,
such as Saturday afternoons. Events like Wimbledon and the Olympics
are in summer, which is also a quiet time for TV.

◉ Sports programmes are much simpler to make than drama or
documentaries. You just film the event and edit the film.

◉ Sport attracts sports fans to TV. Many of them might not otherwise
bother watching.

◉ It also attracts advertisers. TV companies can charge more for their
advertising slots during big sports events.

TV AND THE PROFESSIONAL ATHLETE

TV has had a big role in the rise of the professional athlete. Professional
athletes get paid for playing sport. Without all the interest and money
generated for sport by TV, many sports could not afford to pay them.
Tennis and golf could not offer such big cash prizes, football clubs could
not afford such huge transfer fees. It is an upward spiral. Sport pays well
to attract 'star' players. These players attract more spectators, TV
viewers and sponsors. This in turn makes more money for sport. But it is
only the top players who make a good living from sport. In the USA, for
example, tennis players below the top 50 find it hard to get by.

BROADCAST RIGHTS

In order to show a sports event, a TV company must pay for broadcast
rights. Payment is usually made to the sport's governing body. If the
company buys exclusive rights to a live sports event, it means no one else
can film it. The company can then sell footage on to other companies.
They may buy just a few minutes to show as highlights.

DIFFERENT KINDS OF TV COMPANIES

◉ **Through your aerial.** The terrestrial companies include BBC, ITV,
Channel Four and Channel Five. They transmit programmes from TV
masts to your TV aerial. You have to pay for a TV licence.

◉ **Satellite.** Sky and Freesat are examples. Information is transmitted via
satellite to your satellite dish. You may have to pay a subscription fee.

◉ **Cable.** Virgin Media is an example. The information is carried along
cables buried below the street, with a line fed into your home. You
have to pay a subscription fee.

◉ **Digital.** All TV is changing from analogue to digital which means
many new channels and services becoming available to everyone.

With satellite and cable, the number of TV channels is growing rapidly.
Several show sport only. In 2008 Sky had four sports channels showing
over 100 current sports as well as classic past events.

Settled in for the afternoon. Lots of people wouldn't bother with TV if it weren't for sport. (But if they watched less TV, would they play more sport?)

With the arrival of satellite TV there's been a huge increase in the amount of sport available to the viewer – if you're prepared to pay the subscription fee.

Although having more sport to watch on TV can be a good thing in that it allows more people to watch, it can have a negative effect. When big spectator events are televised live, many people prefer to stay at home and watch in comfort rather than pay for a ticket. As a result, crowd sizes go down. This can have a negative effect on the players as well as affecting gate receipts.

COMPETITION BETWEEN TV COMPANIES

With the increase in TV channels, competition for broadcast rights is fierce. The bids are getting higher each time. In 2002 the BBC signed a £70 million deal for Six Nations rugby coverage for three years. In 2007 it reportedly cost them £160 million to extend their coverage to 2013. Sky television paid an estimated £240 million for the majority of the TV rights for Champions League football up to 2012. Football clubs like Leeds United and Manchester United have their own television channels and so maybe they will soon have exclusive rights to their own matches.

GOVERNMENT INTERVENTION

Satellite, digital and cable companies are ready to pay huge sums for exclusive rights to popular events such as Wimbledon and the FA Cup final. This means that people who don't have a satellite dish or cable TV might not see them at all, or at best just the highlights. Is this fair? Politicians don't think so. The Broadcasting Bill of 1996 sets out the events to which everyone with a TV set should have full access. The list will be continually updated.

PAY-PER-VIEW

The first ever pay-per-view event in the UK was the world heavy-weight title fight in 1996 between Frank Bruno and Mike Tyson. It was shown on BSkyB. Viewers had to book in advance and pay extra on top of their normal subscription. Since then there have been a number of pay-per-view events. However they have caused controversy with people being unhappy about having to pay for an event when they already pay to subscribe to that channel anyway. BSkyB introduced pay-per-view premiership football in 2001.

INTERACTIVE TV

Interactive TV is now on the increase, giving you more control over what you watch. You can switch camera angles during a sports event, choose which sport to watch, listen to alternative commentary and get more information on the sport and players. TV systems that include a hard drive allow you to pause live TV or even rewind it to create your own action replay.

LIST OF EVENTS TO WHICH EVERYONE SHOULD HAVE FULL TV ACCESS

The Derby
The FIFA World Cup finals
The FA Cup Final
The Grand National
The Olympic Games
The finals week of Wimbledon
The Scottish FA Cup Final (in Scotland)
European Football Championship Final
Rugby League Challenge Cup Final
Rugby World Cup Final

QUESTIONS

1 Describe three ways in which sport benefits TV.

2 What does **exclusive rights** mean?

3 Name: **a** one terrestrial broadcast company **b** one satellite broadcast company.

4 What does pay-per-view mean?

Discussion work

5 Do you think it would be a good idea to allow football clubs to have exclusive TV rights to their own matches?

13.5   SPORTING BEHAVIOUR

● ● ● ● In this unit you will learn about the importance of sportsmanship and good behaviour.

SPORTSMANSHIP

Sportsmanship can be defined as playing to the rules and the spirit of the game. We all have to play to the rules but sometimes we see people push those rules to the limit. The rules of tennis, for example, allow players to serve underarm but nobody expects it to happen. In the girls' Wimbledon competition of 2008, a frustrated Slovakian player called Romana Tabakova took Briton Laura Robson by surprise by serving underarm to win a game. Her unsporting behaviour didn't pay off as Laura went on to win the match and the competition.

SPORTS ETIQUETTE

A sport has written rules. But it also has **etiquette** – an unwritten code of good behaviour. For example:

◎ In golf you are quiet when your opponent is playing a shot.

◎ When a football player is injured, the ball may be kicked out of play on purpose so that the casualty can get treatment. When play resumes, it is usually given back to the team who kicked it out.

These are not rules. You don't have to behave this way. They are to do with a sporting attitude and a sense of fair play. What effect do you think they have among the players?

Some examples of etiquette have virtually died out. In cricket, traditionally seen as a 'gentleman's game', a batsman is expected to walk if he knows he is out. When examples of it occur now, it causes much controversy.

VIOLENCE AMONG PLAYERS

In some sports you hardly ever hear of athletes being rude or violent during events. Athletics, swimming and gymnastics are examples. But in other sports violence is quite common. In 2005 Lewis Moody, England and Leicester Rugby Union player, received a six week ban for punching an opponent during a club match. In 2007 footballer Joey Barton got a four month suspended jail sentence for assaulting a team mate during training. Violence among players damages a sport. It is the job of the club managers, coaches and governing bodies to curb it. This is particularly important if players are to feel safe when playing.

One example of tennis etiquette. Definitely not a rule of the game!

THE ROLE OF SPECTATORS

As a spectator you can help sport but you can also harm it. Football hooligans are an example. They ruin events by fighting opposing fans, throwing things onto the pitch and even sending death threats to players and officials. English fans in particular have had a bad reputation but this seems to be improving over recent years. If the fans are violent the team is often punished so teams are working hard to remove hooliganism from their sport.

ROLE MODELS AND PARTICIPATION

Whether they like it or not sportsmen and sportswomen are seen as role models to young people. If a sport has a good role model they can been seen as an ambassador for that sport. When a team or an individual does well in a sport, participation increases. The tiny country of Jamaica put their sprinting success in the Beijing Olympics partly down to earlier role models performing well for other countries. Colin Jackson and Linford Christie both have family links to Jamaica. Their success for Great Britain inspired Jamaican youngsters to take up athletics too.

ROLE MODELS AND BEHAVIOUR

To be a positive role model it is important to be seen to behave well both on and off the field of play as a role model's behaviour is often copied by young people. An extremely important factor here is the response to the officials by competitors, coaches, spectators and TV commentators. Some sports have more of a problem here than others. For example in Rugby Union, if a player shows dissent or tries to argue a decision with the referee they immediately lose 10 metres. Football, however, has a bad reputation when it comes to the players' attitude towards the officials. In the 2008/09 season, the FA told the referees to be stricter with players who argued in an attempt to increase respect in the game.

Will the campaign by the FA for referees to be stricter with players increase respect towards officials?

QUESTIONS

1 Give two examples of sporting etiquette that are not mentioned here.

2 What is meant by sportsmanship? Give an example of good sportsmanship from your sport.

3 What is a role model? How do they impact on participation?

4 How does someone become a good role model for their sport? Think about their behaviour as well as their performance.

5 How does good behaviour improve people's safety?

6 In cricket batsmen used to 'walk' when they knew they were out. Do you think we should return to this attitude?

Discussion work

7 Look at your sport. Who are the good role models? Are there any bad role models?

QUESTIONS ON CHAPTER 13

1 True or false? Explain your answer.
   a If you are an amateur athlete it means you are not as good as the professionals.
   b Amateur athletes in athletics can't accept prize money.
   c Appearance money is what you get for wearing your sponsor's logo.
   d Both amateur and professional golfers can compete in an open golf tournament.
   e Open sports never offer prize money.
   f If no-one wanted to watch sport there would be no professionals.

2 According to the technical definition, is the athlete below amateur or professional?
   a Andy Murray
   b James DeGale
   c Christina Ohuruogu
   d Bradley Wiggins
   e Tom Daley

3 a Explain how Trust Funds operate in amateur athletics.
   b Rugby Union used to run Trust Funds. It stopped doing so in 1995. Why was this?

4 a Is sponsorship always in the form of money? Explain.
   b Top sports stars are paid a lot to endorse products such as sports shoes and soft drinks.
      i What does endorse mean?
      ii Why are companies prepared to pay them for this?
   c Give one example of product endorsement by an athlete.

5 Give reasons for these statements:
   a Sponsors prefer to sponsor sports events shown on TV.
   b Sponsors are more prepared to sponsor men's sport than women's.
   c An unknown young athlete will find it difficult to get sponsorship.
   d A gymnastics competition is more likely to get sponsorship than a women's rugby event.
   e A sponsor is likely to cancel a contract with an athlete who is caught doping.

6 Sponsorship in sport is very common. Describe, using an example, how sponsorship can be an advantage to the sport and how it can promote participation.

7 Some companies would find it very difficult to sponsor sport because of the products they sell. Give two examples and explain why.

8 a List everything that comes under the heading the media.
   b Which medium has most impact on sport? Why? Give at least two reasons to support your answer.

9 The radio provides a fair amount of sports coverage.
   a What advantages does radio have over TV? List as many as you can.
   b Now list its disadvantages compared with TV.

10 a Make a table with two columns like this:

Benefits to me of watching sport on TV	Benefits to me of playing sport myself

   b Now fill in as many benefits as you can in each column.
   c Which brings more benefits?
   d What advice would you give people who spend hours watching sport on TV?

11 Sports events can sometimes appear more exciting when shown on TV than they are in real life. Explain why.

12 Television promotes and broadcasts sport in many ways, such as documentaries. Give two other ways in which television covers sport and give an example of each.

13 Role models can have both a positive and negative effect on participation and performance. Give two positive and two negative qualities of role models.

14 tennis   gymnastics   swimming
   rugby   volleyball   football
   a From this list choose the two sports where you think:
      i violence between participants is most likely
      ii violence between participants is least likely
      iii violence among spectators is most likely
      iv violence among spectators is least likely
   b Do you think there is a connection between violence among spectators and the nature of the sport?
   c How could you test this theory?
   d Design a project for this purpose. Describe it as fully as you can.

15 'Football causes violence.' Do you agree? Explain why.

APPLIED QUESTION

A16 Jemma is a successful professional athlete who trains full time in order to compete in the marathon for England and Great Britain. She needs sponsorship in order to be able to afford to do this. Describe:
   a How easily, or not, she will have found it to get a sponsor.
   b How her sponsor will be linked with the media.
   c How the media might be a help or hindrance to her.
   d What might happen if she starts to regularly underperform?

THINGS TO DO

Amateur versus professional in sport

The division between amateurs and professionals had its origins in the class system. **Amateurs** were gentlemen who could afford to play a sport, often full time, for pleasure. **Professionals** were lower-class people who earned money from sport, often by doing something for a **wager** (bet) or by competing for prizes against others. For example, gentlemen with coaches and horses had footmen. If you were the gambling type you might choose an athletic footman, and pay him something to compete in walking races against your friends' footmen. You'd put a bet on the race.

Cricket was popular among gentlemen. In the 18th century gentlemen's cricket clubs employed some lower-class cricketers who were called **players**. They were paid to look after the grounds, coach the gentlemen and play against them in matches.

As sports became more organised, tension between the amateur gentlemen and working-class professionals grew. In 1866 the Amateur Athletics Club was set up by gentlemen. Working-class men were excluded because it was felt manual labour gave them an advantage in strength.

In 1880 the club became the Amateur Athletics Association. It redefined an amateur as someone who gained no financial reward from a sport. The working class was allowed in.

1   a Find out more about the early professional cricketers. Write a short essay about them.
     b Find a copy of an old poster for a match between gentlemen and players. What do you notice about the way their names are listed?

2   A famous example of someone walking for a wager was Captain Barclay. In 1800 he walked 1000 miles in 1000 hours for 1000 guineas. Try to find out more about Captain Barclay. Who put up the money? Where did he walk?

3   Find out more about the Amateur Athletics Club. Who started it? In what sports did it compete, and where? Write a short essay about it.

Sponsorship

4   a   Make a table with these headings:

Sport	Team or individual	Sponsor	Nature of sponsor's business

     b   Now fill it in for as many sports and sponsors as you can.
     c   Look at the last column for each sport. Can you see any relationship between the sponsor's business and the sport? If yes, explain it.

Media coverage of sport

5   The work in this activity should be shared among the class.
     a Six people each collect one newspaper a day for a week (Monday to Saturday). The papers should be a mixture of tabloids and broadsheets (quality papers). One person collects *The Guardian*, another *The Sun* and so on.
     b For each newspaper make a table like the one started here:

Name of newspaper: *The Independent*		
Sport	Type	Number of articles
Football	Men's	IIII III
	Women's	II
Rugby	Men's	III
	Women's	

     c Go through all the sport pages in your set of papers. (A new person can take over for each copy.) For each article on sport, put a tally mark in the table.
     d Now add up the tally marks for each sport. Put the results in a table like this:

Total number of articles in *The Independent* for the week		
Sport	Men's	Women's
Football	54	

     e Show the results as a bar chart. Put the women's sports at one end of the chart and the men's at the other. Put each in order, the sport with most coverage first.
     f Study the bar chart. Which sports get most coverage? Which get least? How well are women's sports covered? Write a report on what you have discovered.

6   Now compare the bar graphs for the different papers.
     a Do the same sports get most coverage in all of them? Which sports are these?
     b Is it true that the quality press provides more coverage of minority sports?
     c Which paper covers most women's sports?
     d Overall, how does coverage of women's sports compare with that of men's? Try to express it as a percentage.

7   Now pick the main sports event of the week. Compare coverage of this event in a quality paper and a tabloid.
     a What differences do you notice?
     b Do you agree with the statements in the table in unit 13.3?

GLOSSARY

Chapter 1

health-related fitness   the fitness for everyday activities and good health.

maximal oxygen consumption   the maximum capacity of the body to transport and use oxygen during exercise.

somatotyping   working out body type from a scale ranging from 1 to 7 for each of three 'somatotypes': endomorph, mesomorph and ectomorph.

VO₂ max   the maximum amount of oxygen that can be delivered to and used by muscles during exercise in one minute.

Chapter 2

aerobic energy   energy produced by the body using oxygen.

aerobic threshold   the exercise intensity at which anaerobic energy pathways start to operate.

aerobic training zone   training in this zone improves aerobic fitness.

anaerobic energy   the production of energy without oxygen.

maximum heart rate   the highest number of times the heart can contract in one minute: the maximum rate your heart can beat. Known as MHR.

oxygen debt   the extra amount of oxygen required after exercise to return the body to its resting state.

target zone   the range of intensity at which the heart needs to work to best develop cardiovascular endurance: usually between 60% and 80% of maximum heart rate.

training thresholds   the lower and upper limits of an effective training zone: work done below the lower level will have little or no effect on the improvement of fitness, work above the higher level can lead to injury.

Chapter 3

cool-down   exercises following strenuous activity to reduce the heart rate, remove lactic acid and repay oxygen debt.

periodisation   organising the training plan into phases or cycles, for example to ensure fitness for a particular competition or for a season.

recovery rate   how quickly your body gets back to normal after exercise.

seasonal   occurring during a particular season or time of year.

warm-up   exercising, stretching, etc., to get the body ready for strenuous activity.

Chapter 4

analgesic   a type of pain-relieving medicine.

anorexia nervosa   an eating disorder in which sufferers become obsessed by thinness and starve themselves to reduce their weight.

anorexic   describing someone who suffers from anorexia nervosa.

basal metabolic rate   the amount of energy used while the body is completely at rest, after all food has been digested.

blood doping   methods of boosting the number of red blood cells (which carry oxygen) in the blood – used illegally to enhance performance.

body composition   the amount of fat, muscle and bone tissue which is present in the body.

bulimia nervosa   an eating disorder in which people binge eat, and then make themselves sick or get rid of what they've eaten in other similar ways.

carboloading   endurance athletes, e.g. marathon runners, use carboloading to increase the store of glycogen in their muscles.

cellulose   comes from plant cell walls: humans can't digest it.

doping   the use of banned performance-enhancing drugs in sport.

glucose   a form of sugar used in cells for energy.

kilocalories   the amount of heat needed to increase the temperature of one kilogram of water by 1 °C.

kilojoules   a measurement of energy.

narcotic   originally meaning any drug produced from opium, it now refers more widely to a family of drugs that have the same general effect of reducing the senses, for example sense of pain.

obese   when excess body fat has built up so much that the person's health can be affected. It is usually defined as a body mass index of 30 kg/m2 or higher.

obesity   the condition of being obese.

overfat   when too much of the body composition is fat: for men: more than 19% of total body composition as fat; for women: more than 26%.

overweight   having weight in excess of normal.

risk assessment   the assessment of how likely a risk of something happening is, including how big the impact of that risk would be under different conditions.

underweight   when someone is under what would be considered a healthy weight for their body type: measured in terms of the body mass index.

working energy   the amount of energy required beyond that needed for the basal metabolic rate; the energy we need to do things.

Chapter 5

abduction   movement away from the centre line of the body.

acute   angles smaller than a right angle (less than 90°) are called acute angles.

adduction   movement towards the centre line of the body.

cartilage   dense connective tissue: can take a long time to heal if damaged.

chronic   something that is persistent, lasts a long time, also something that develops slowly: often used for medical conditions.

extension   straightening a joint.

flexion   bending a joint.

growth hormone   a hormone that stimulates growth and cell reproduction.

growth plates (epiphyseal plates)   growing parts of bones or joints, found in children. These then ossify (turn to 'normal' bone) in adults.

joint capsule   a sort of envelope surrounding and protecting a synovial joint.

joint cavity   a small gap between the bones that is filled by synovial fluid.

joints   where two or more bones meet.

ligaments   elastic tissue connecting bone to bone, stabilising movement at joints.

osteoblasts   a type of cell responsible for bone formation.

osteoclasts   a type of cell responsible for reabsorbing bone.

RICE   Rest, Ice, Compression, Elevation – a way of treating injured ligaments or muscles.

synovial joints   a joint containing synovial fluid which allows a range of movement.

synovial membrane   the soft tissue that lines surfaces without cartilage in synovial joints.

Chapter 6

active stretching   a type of stretching in which you extend limbs beyond their normal range.

agonist   the muscle that contracts to produce movement.

antagonistic   muscles that work with the prime mover/agonist to control movement at joints. As the agonist contracts the antagonist relaxes and vice versa.

cardiac muscle   heart muscle: beats without tiring – until it stops!

fast twitch   muscle fibres that provide fast, powerful contractions, but tire easily: mainly used for anaerobic activity.

fatigue   temporary loss of strength and energy resulting from hard physical or mental work.

flexibility   the ability of your joints to move through a full range of motion.

isometric contraction   muscular contraction that results in no movement at a joint, muscle contracts but fibres remain the same length.

isometric training   training methods that use isometric contractions.

isotonic contraction   muscular contraction that causes movement at a joint.

isotonic training training methods that use isotonic contractions.

muscle tone the amount of tension or resistance to movement in a muscle; what enables us to keep our bodies in a certain position.

passive stretching flexibility exercise: stretching by pushing against something.

skeletal muscle muscles of the skeleton that are under voluntary control.

slow twitch muscle fibres that provide slower, less powerful contractions but can keep working for long periods of time: used mainly in aerobic exercise.

smooth muscle muscles of the internal organs which work automatically.

static strength strength involving isometric muscular actions in which the length of the muscle does not change and there is no visible movement at the joint.

static stretching used to stretch muscles while the body is at rest. Various techniques gradually lengthen a muscle to an elongated position (to the point of discomfort); the stretch is then held for 10-30 seconds.

striped muscle skeletal muscles of the body.

tendons fibrous tissue that joins a muscle to bone.

voluntary muscles muscles that work under our direct control.

Chapter 7

antibodies cells used by the immune system to identify and destroy foreign objects, such as bacteria and viruses.

bacteria microorganisms that are found in every habitat on earth and throughout the human body. Some cause illness and disease, some are helpful, some are neutral.

blood vessels tubes that transport blood around the body.

carotid an artery that supplies the head and neck with oxygenated blood.

circulatory system the blood distribution network.

evaporate when a liquid vapourises; turns from a liquid into a gas.

heart the organ that pumps blood around the body.

heart rate the number of heart beats per minute: changes with exercise.

heat stroke the body is good at getting rid of excess heat but heat stroke occurs when it cannot get rid of all the excess heat it is experiencing or producing; body temperature climbs higher and higher – a medical emergency.

hypothermia this is when the body's temperature drops below the level needed for normal bodily functions.

phagocytes cells that destroy pathogens (germs) as part of the body's immune system.

pulmonary circulation the movement of deoxygenated blood from the heart to the lungs, where carbon dioxide is exchanged for oxygen, and oxygenated blood is returned to the heart.

pulse the beating of heart, felt at arteries near the surface of the body.

pulse point a point at which the pulse can be felt.

radial artery in the forearm.

radiation when energy emitted by one source travels through a space and is absorbed by something else.

systemic circulation movement of oxygenated blood from the heart to the rest of the body, and the return of deoxygenated blood to the heart.

vascular shunt the redistribution of blood to skeletal muscle to meet the demands of exercise.

vasoconstriction the narrowing of blood vessels, used to conserve body heat.

vasoldilation the widening of blood vessels, used to get rid of excess heat.

viruses these are infections of cells that cannot survive outside of their host cell. They don't all cause illnesses but many do and they are fought by the immune system; vaccines can also protect against viruses.

Chapter 8

expiration breathing out air and waste products.

hypertrophy the increase of the size of an organ or in a select area of the tissue as its cells grow bigger.

inspiration breathing air into the lungs.

respiratory rate the number of breaths per minute.

tidal volume the amount of air breathed in and out during normal breathing.

vital capacity the maximum amount of air that can be forcibly exhaled after breathing in as much as possible.

Chapter 9

closed skill skills not affected by the environment.

co-ordinated organised, working together as a system, skilful, graceful.

feedback information about the outcome of a performance.

input something going into a system.

open skill skill affected by the environment, so that change according to circumstances.

pre-determined set in advance.

Chapter 10

extrinsic motivation motivation that comes from factors outside an individual.

intrinsic motivation motivation that comes from an individual themselves.

Chapter 11

5x60 initiative a Welsh initiative for sport in schools: 60 minutes of activity, 5 times a week.

job-share when two or more people do the same job at different times of the week.

target groups specific groups of the population with similar characteristics or interests.

Chapter 12

corporate tax taxes on the profits made by companies.

income tax tax on what people earn: those who earn above certain bands pay more.

sports councils government agencies responsible for developing sports in each nation.

value added tax (VAT) a complicated tax that is based on the difference between a commodity's price before taxes and its cost of production. It is an indirect tax: you pay it when you buy things rather than paying it directly to the taxman.

Chapter 13

amateur someone who takes part in an activity, e.g. a sport, as a pastime rather than as a profession.

etiquette customs or rules about how to behave correctly in a social event.

quality press the non-tabloid press: newspapers like *The Independent*, *The Guardian*, *The Times*.

sponsorship a business relationship between a company that supports a sportsperson or team in return for the opportunity to advertise in association with that sportsperson or team.

tabloid press 'tabloid' actually means the shape of newspapers but it also describes a more sensationalist approach to news than the non-tabloid press go for (though it is not always easy to tell the difference).

tax-deductible something that can be offset against the amount of tax you need to pay.

trust fund where money (or any kind of property) is managed by one person for another.